EDITH C

A
BLACK COUNTRY
NURSE
AT LARGE

A BLACK COUNTRY SOCIETY PUBLICATION
49 VICTORIA ROAD, TIPTON, STAFFS.

First Impression November 1973
Second Impression September 1974
Third Impression March 1976

1 SBN 0 904015 01 7

Cover: L. BAKER (Clebak)

Printed by Reliance Printing Works, Halesowen, West Midlands.

To every patient I
ever had.

Bless 'em all.

If you find anything in the book to offend, please accept my regrets. Incidents of patients themselves are dropped into it like ingredients into a Christmas pudding and stirred well before serving. No any one patient is specified, and as far as I can remember no name used is that of anyone I have attended.

If you are of Black Country origin be proud of it, for Black Country people are of the salt of the earth and many of the much maligned words peculiar to them can be traced back to Chaucer.

My remuneration for the book is donated to the Black Country Society which, during these ' winds of change ' does so much to preserve our individuality.

1.

I am a district nurse of long standing, and for many years have plodded a black country beat. Patients can be a pleasure or a thorn in the flesh, but no matter which, if you attend long enough, you become fond of them.

Mrs. Tibbs was one of the thorns, but there was a bond between us which was a combination of affection and armed neutrality. She was a randy old warhorse, squabbling with all and sundry, and thriving on the belligerency. Despite being very handicapped she lived alone, and if she had any relatives they had long since learned to keep their distance.

When the meals-on-wheels service got into full swing it seemed just the thing and I persuaded her to try it out.

The wheels were represented by a van which was chauffered by a military type retired gentleman and the ' meals ' were produced by a brisk lady in green. Whenever I saw them, the meals looked piping hot and delicious, but Mrs. Tibbs yammered peevishly: " I cor ate nairen." They were " riffy " or the " taters wor dun."

She also speculated evilly on what went on between the military gent and the lady in green. " I sid 'em," she leered, " carryin' on up the coppice. The bawdy beesom! As fer 'im, 'e's nowt but a bloody ponce! Bugger me, if 'er aye got the welfare bloke in the van now I'm never 'ere. Ten ter one 'e'll be theer 'til tew o'clock. The strumpet! An' 'im a mon wi' fower kids! "

In vain I defended their morals, threatened her with slander, or simply turned a deaf ear. " No good tellin' yo' nuthin'," she grieved. " An' me a poor widder woman, clammed ter jeth an' wi' me fittle 'arf cooked. No wonder me bally's all of a wamble."

One morning I arrived to be confronted with a pea on a saucer.

" Theer! " Mrs. Tibbs indicated it triumphantly. " Ketch ote o' that! Cost ate it? I bet yo' cor! "

Tentatively I squeezed the pea between thumb and forefinger and agreed; it was like a bibble. But she was not to be put off with that. " Doh ivver-ovver! " she bellucked, " Yo'n got teeth wot I air. Yo' try bitin' on it! "

Nothing less would satisfy her and I had no time for gammiting. Gingerly I bit hard on the offending pea, which immediately shot across the room. " Theer! " she rejoiced hugging herself, " Yo' cor ate it, con yer? An' what's more it's bin threw me once! "

*　　*　　*

When Doctor Quinn arrived green from Ireland, and with a brogue that could be cut with a knife, it caused much consternation amongst the patients he had inherited. " The fule," they chuntered, " 'E cor even spake praper, 'E's bloody daft! "

He in turn suffered frustration. " Oi'll niver understand them," he mourned. " They're for iver tellin' me they've not been to the ground. What in hell's name d'ya make o' that? "

Loyal to the locals, I expressed surprise that he, a medical man, did not recognise such a common term for constipation.

" Holy Mither o' God! " he keened. " You're but another of 'em, an' here's me thinkin' all nurses are Oirish! "

In an effort to make themselves better understood, patients bawled at the top of their voices; symptoms and sufferings were shouted aloud and the surgery waiting room became a place of entertainment. Hitherto secret ailments were disclosed to all and sundry. These were compensations indeed!

Mr. Wagstaff was a patient of Doctor Quinns' and Mr. Wagstaff had pneumonia. He had got it specifically to annoy Mrs. Wagstaff, for she resented having strangers traipsing about her immaculate house. In particular, she abhorred Doctor Quinn, whose feet were very large and whose boots were always muddy. Poor man, he had no wife to clean them.

6

Nurses, she regarded with suspicion as being no better than they should be. After all, when you thought of the things they did to folks! No self respecting woman would be a nurse.

Mrs. Wagstaff's mother and sister, replicas of herself, were part of the household and the three martinets darted about before me strewing newspapers where I might tread. " Arter all," reflected the old mother sotto vocce, " yo' doh know where 'ers bin! " Poor Mr. Wagstaff, my heart went out to him.

In my earlier days, pneumonia patients had a lysis and a crisis. They were propped up in Fowler's position and their labouring chests suffered the added burden of kaolin poultices. In recent years, antibiotics have taken over, and a course of intramuscular injections, dexterously aimed at the tenderest part of the posterior, usually get the sufferers on their feet in a week, (No doubt propelled there by their tortured buttocks!) Mr. Wagstaff was the exception to the rule; he did not respond to treatment and his malaise dragged on. Neighbours talked darkly of the insurance policies with which he had been backed.

One morning my visit coincided with that of Doctor Quinn. I groaned inwardly and edged for the door, but anticipating my escape, he took my arm and drew me outside onto the landing, followed by the relatives with ears cocked and eyes agog.

" Oi'll consult with nurse alone, please," he said, and motioning me into the adjoining bathroom, closed the door on their frustrated faces.

Mrs. Wagstaff's bathroom was as prim as herself and camouflaged with much candlewick. A prissy pink cover did its best to disguise the lavatory seat, and on this the young medico perched himself with a cigarette while I sat angled on the edge of the bath. Concern increased within me; however would I make up for lost time?

Having secured a captive audience, Doctor Quinn waxed eloquent, oblivious to the fact that half the time I could not follow his jargon anyway. Outside, creaking floorboards reminded us of the waiting relatives. When his second cigarette had gone up in smoke, Doctor Quinn finally prised himself off his perch on the pedestal and automatically, before I could stop him, pulled the dangling chain.

As the water flushed noisesomely, we stared at each other in horror. Outside, a stoney silence condemned us. There was only one way out — through the door. Sheepishly, we took it.

7

To the scandalised faces of the three women outside an explanation was futile, and if we had committed the most gross indecency we could not have looked more guilty.

Mr. Wagstaff made a reluctant recovery and Doctor Quinn left for pastures new, but whenever our paths cross the pursed lips of Mrs. Wagstaff show that she has not forgotten and, fool that I am, I blush.

*   *   *

Some of the oldest houses still defying demolition had been built to house the prolific Victorians. Poker faced facades overlooked narrow streets and back entrances opened onto a communal yard, the playground of innumerable children and commonly known as the fode.

Such a building housed the Finnegans. The family consisted of Ma and Pa, nine assorted offspring, Gran'ma Finnegan and a widowed uncle known as Gaffer. Gran'ma was stone deaf, hearing aids were quite ineffectual, no sound pierced her silent world and I think she was thankful for the protection her deafness provided. She smiled and nodded and obligingly buttered " pieces " for her grandchildren.

Gaffer was the original tenant. Years ago on the death of his wife, his niece had moved in to do for him. When she later became espoused to the fertile Finnegan it was taken for granted that her husband and mother-in-law should move in too. Gaffer however, clung with the tenacity of the aged to his rent book, and one day he told me how he first came by it.

He was, he said, a young masher out walking with his girl when they passed the house which had been recently vacated. Houses were two a penny, with even a rent free week for scrubbing it out.

" Ween a' that," he joked, pointing to the empty house.

" Dun yer main it? " she asked.

" Arr," he laughed, and thought no more of it.

But when they met the following night: " We con a' that," she said.

" A' wot? " he asked, mystified.

" That 'ouse yer fule! " She had had his name put in the rent book. Come Sunday the banns were up and before he knew it he was wed. Now his rent book warded off the shadow of the " werkus " and he slept with it under his pillow

8

Ma Finnegan, after each succeeding pregnancy (and strangely enough Pa was a nightwatchman), had complications with her bosom. This is where I came in; but now she had been sterilized, and the offending bosom " took off."

The last baby, a son rejoicing in the name of Jasper, was a puny child quite unlike his namesake, a superman who romped cartoon-wise through the pages of a popular daily, but he survived.

Although Ma no longer needed my ministrations there was nearly always someone in the family who did, and now poor Gaffer was getting trouble with his waterworks. " Arr well, it doh seem like wum if yo' bay acummin'," mused Ma happily. No doubt she missed our cast off clouts when I was not coming in.

One day, when writing a report for Gaffer's doctor, I consulted the newspaper which did service as a table cloth for the date. " Let's see, today's the fourth isn't it? " I calculated.

" Arr! " grieved Ma, " Ower Jasper musta bin five yesterdee. Aye it a shairm? 'E day arf 'ave a lampin! " With a rush of maternal affection she clutched the bewildered child to her remaining bosom and wiped his snotty nose on her apron.

The next day I took a few discarded toys for Jasper, but he was gone. His fifth birthday, now remembered, was a milestone, and he had been despatched with his brothers and sisters to school. The Finnegan brood qualified for free dinners.

The next day, I asked Ma how he had got on at school. " God a'mighty! " she shrieked, " Yo' 'ad orter sid 'im doh 'arf think 'e's somebody now! Why 'e cum wum yesterdee . . . waented 'is tay off a plairt! "

*　　*　　*

Martha Gamp, when I first beheld her, was a benign octogenarian newly scrubbed and released from hospital. She might well have qualified as a candidate when Whistler painted his mum, it was not until she opened her mouth that she let the cat out of the bag.

She greeted me with an enthusiasm which never flagged during the twelve years I attended her, but her daughters of whom she had five, she lashed with a vitriolic temper. Ben, her only son, forty and unmarried, alone remained at home and she regarded him with utter contempt. He was a shift worker and took refuge in his bed. His miserable life was compensated by his incredible ability to sleep and he was the only man I ever knew who overlay himself when he was on two 'til ten.

That I found favour with Mrs. Gamp stemmed from the fact that she had for the greater part of her active life enjoyed the status of a self appointed midwife and local layer out, and she regarded me as the medium through which she intended to convey her ancient lore to an ignorant posterity. Since she was a diabetic needing daily insulin, general nursing care and a weekly bath, she had ample time in which to impart her knowledge.

It was customary except in country areas for general nurses and midwives to work apart to lessen risk of infection, but Mrs. Gamp deplored this as a lot of bunkum and rejoiced when some complication such as measles in the house or infection in a mother or baby, even 'flu, necessitated my taking a case over from the midwife. Then she could give me the full benefit of her knowledge.

The mother must be kept on slops for three days, bound firmly with a bolster case and confined to her bed for three weeks, after which everything went " back with a click." She must be warned against letting the child glimpse itself in a mirror before its first birthday or until then, cutting its finger nails; the mother was advised to nibble them and of course she must never enter another's house until she had been churched! To ensure good eyesight, a spot of urine should be instilled into the infant's eyes, and in the case of girl babies there was an essential ritual known as " breaking the nipple strings," on which I will not elaborate.

In my routine work, she instructed me on the making of cow-pat poultices (unparalleled for retaining the heat), " hungry water " — a soap liniment smelling strongly of camphor, and foxglove tea. The latter was in great demand for sufferers of bald patches on the scalp: they were instructed to rub it into the afflicted areas twice daily and strangely enough, it was most effective. Not all that strange maybe: digitalis is derived from the foxglove; or maybe the stimulation of the scalp massage contributed to the cure.

Then, of course, there was the all important technique of " laying out" a la Gamp, and the warning that if the corpse was inclined to " soss " another death in the family was imminent.

10

Ma Gamp's much maligned daughters were grand women and though whipped constantly by their mother's virulent tongue, they arranged, rota wise, to cope with her household chores. They were all married, and it was their offspring who were delegated to harvest the herbs in their various seasons. Ma, now unable to negotiate the stairs, occupied the parlour together with her bed and commode, and all the family trembled in her presence.

Poor Ben suffered from habitual constipation which was not helped by his inactivity. Frequently he was subjected to enemas saponis, to the disgust of his parent. "The girt loon!" she ranted, urging me to lace the soapy water with black treacle which she maintained would "agitate 'is guts," and not only produce the desired result, but would "gi' 'im sich a bally airk, 'e wo' niver waent another!"

Ben, though sparse of speech, boasted a colourful vocabulary and, after all, a good cussing does much to lower the blood pressure. Once, under the misery of a manual evacuation, he called me a "Fuckin' lousebound bastard," and though later, when relieved, he said shamefacedly: "I day mane it nus," I was stirred by the sheer poetry of the epithet and for long after, when having to sign my name, to S.R.N. I added F.L.B. Nobody ever questioned it. Perhaps, like the story of the king in the "altegether," they hesitated to air their ignorance.

Ma Gamp, daily anticipating her demise, dictated to us all as to the disposal of her cadaver. Cremation was definitely off. "If yo' bern me I'll ornt yer!" she threatened, "I'm agooin' up Ockabonk, in the cherchyard on top o' yer ferther." She cackled evilly: "That'll shairk 'im, me on top!"

Her daughters, discomforted, avoided each other's gaze and shushed the children out to play on the "fo'd." If she began reminiscing, there was no knowing what might be revealed.

One morning, towards midday, I was attending another patient in the vicinity, when a neighbour of the Gamps arrived. "See o'd Martha's gone at last," she volunteered. "Never!" I cried. "She was lively enough when I was there a couple of hours ago!" "Well 'er doh look very lively now," ejaculated the woman, and went on to describe how, on seeing the curtains drawn, she had investigated and found Martha dead. She had roused Ben and despatched him to summon the rest of the family.

11

She regarded me quizzically, " 'Er'd bin layed owt a trate. If yo' day dew it, 'ew did? "

Perplexed, I hurried off to investigate. As she had stated, the curtains were drawn, and in the darkened room the family stood surveying the sheeted form on the bed.

" P'raps it's for the best," they said with ill concealed relief.

" Thank God! " came from a more outspoken son-in law.

Reverently, I turned back the sheet revealing the aged face, the jaw expertly bound with a large white handkerchief, the eyelids expertly weighted with the traditional pennies. One penny slipped eschew, a hoary eye gazed into mine, and the corpse, struggling with its trappings croaked: " Ayve me up, nus, I wanta piddle."

Two daughters rushed shrieking into the street, one fainted clean away, another begun to have hysterics. Ben was the first to recover. " Strewth! " he breathed, " I goo ter the bottom of ower stairs! "

Mrs. Gamp was unabashed. Now enthroned upon her commode, she hugged herself. " Med a good job o' mesen, day I nus? As fer yo' buggers," she addressed the remnants of her family, " Cotched yo' lot proper day I? 'Agglin' over me divi' afore I'm co'd! Nor yer wo' git me 'surance book neether, I'n bernt it! "

" Doh knock on! " cried the long suffering son-in-law, " When time does cum tha' wo' be left above ground, not if I 'as ter bury yer mesen! "

When time " did come " it was peacefully in her sleep at the age of ninety-two. With my last job for her completed, she lay serene and strangely quiescent, her eyelids in repose without the need of pennies. Her silver hair, bound with my daughter's white ribbons, shone like a halo.

The family eyed her warily, and fearful of another resurrection, begged me to attend the funeral. To be on the safe side, they kept her for two weeks before burial.

Fortunately the weather was cold.

*　　*　　*

After his mother's death, Ben, freed from lifelong tyranny, was like a ship without a rudder. His sisters did for him as they had done for their mother, and persuaded him to keep the home on. He was not much cop, but you never know, he might pick up with somebody.

Ben picked up with an old work-mate, Joby. They spent their leisure in the local and in the warm atmosphere of bonhommie and badinage, Ben bloomed. Even his bowels, stimulated by the influx of beer, began to function with regularity.

At times of calamity and carnage, Joby was wont to say: " Yo' aye sairf outside a pub! " It was ironic, therefore, that one night, in the middle of his pint and an animated anecdote, his eyes became glazed and, still clutching his tankard, he slid slowly down onto the floor, slopping the contents all over himself. His mouth was agape and his dentures awry, gawping with an air of astonishment at being so suddenly precipitated into the hereafter.

Natural causes, they said, " Worra luvly way ter goo," commiserated his cronies and collected for a vacant chair composed of moss and heather.

" In the midst of life we are in death," philosophised the vicar. Ben was shattered. He sought to comfort himself with a prayer, but all he could recall was a childhood jingle:

" For thy coming Lord we pray,
But let it be some other day,
On thy return our hopes are set,
Thy will be done, but not just yet."

And somehow, that hardly seemed appropriate in the circumstances.

Ben went on the box. He had lost his taste for his beer and was unable to stomach his fittle. Mooching and emanciated, he brooded over an empty grate. As his sisters said: " A mon had fallen off him." Deprived of his liquor, he became constipated again and once more I was sent for. I hoped we were not going to get started on that enema lark again and suggested that glycerine suppositories might do the trick. " Naow," said Ben morosely, " They bay no gud. The doctor gid me some but I 'ad sich a job ter get um down me."

Even when we got the point of entry sorted out they proved ineffective.

When Ben began to complain of a niggling pain where the layman thinks his stomach is, his doctor sent him to the hospital for investigation. There it was decided that he should go for an X-ray with a barium enema. Barium is an opaque substance, so that when given as an enema and retained, the bowel, with any abnormalities, is shown up clearly on the X-ray plate.

13

Preparation for X-ray is the job of the district nurse and necessitates giving the patient an enema the previous evening, followed by a washout on the morning of the X-ray itself. Ben was well accustomed to enemas and when I explained that the washout the following morning was merely to ensure that his bowel was clean, he quite understood the need. His bowel would have to be clean he agreed. " Like chicklings," he said. " 'Ow wull they dew it nus? " he asked anxiously, " No coddin' now! "

I explained the simplicty of it all, but he didn't believe me. " I cor fairse it, nus, I shor goo! " and fear leaked out of his eyes.

This wasn't Ben. I sat down beside him and took his horny hand. " Tell me Ben, what exactly did they say at the hospital? " Ben gulped. " The doctor said, ' Yo' cum up a Thursday an' we'll have a luk at yer innards on a plairt! "

*   *   *

Miss Fallows' spacious Victorian house lay well back from the main road and was approached by means of a long over-grown driveway. The bell on the shabbily elegant front door did not respond, of course, but I found a back entrance and finally tracked down my new patient in a room which must once have been the kitchen. Obviously, it was here she chose to live, and from the single bed in the corner, to sleep also. She was huddled in an old armchair by the fire and wore a cloche hat, a mangy fur coat and a pair of combinations. On her legs, old Lisle stockings adhered stickily to the ulcers which were my special problem.

I introduced myself and she received me graciously. Everyone, she said, had been so kind. A lady in green had been only a little while ago to clean her room and to cook her a meal. There had once, she reminisced, been many servants, with a nanny and later a governess for herself. She had been an only child, but after her parents died investments had gone wrong, money had evaporated. When the last family retainer had died also, she had engaged a certain person to " do for her " but the person had not been satisfactory and had persisted in bringing her unruly brood of children with her. Now, she was alone, except for a young woman who did her shopping. The price of food was scandalous, but she ate very little and it was obvious that she suffered from malnutrition. It was obvious, too, that she suffered from fleas.

14

Brittle black particles encrusted the tops of her stockings, and when I cautiously turned them down, pediculosis corpus frolicked in abundance. Never had I seen so many fleas! Startled by the daylight, they leapt in all directions, particularly mine. Quickly, I peeled off the stockings and threw them on the fire, but by now they had invaded the " combs." As for the fur coat! I shuddered to think!

When I had prepared a basin of disinfectant and a bowl of hot water, I began the formidable task of cleansing Miss Fallow. She seemed surprisingly unperturbed. " I suppose you get a lot of this," she said. Fleas still cavorted (even cohabited!) undiminished, and I dropped them ruthlessly into the disinfectant. Poor things, they'd had such an idyllic existence until now, and they could not help being fleas. (I always did have a leaning towards Buddhism and the belief in sanctity of life, however humble). It was obvious, however, that I was fighting a losing battle. I confessed to her that I would have to report the fleas to the authorities, they were too prolific for me to deal with and I must protect the other patients. She did not protest. Worse was to come. When I came to remove the cloche hat, it was stuck fast. I prised it off and found why; her hair was cemented solid with nits and the excreta of multitudinous pediculosis capitus (" bogies " to the layman). The only thing was to clip off all her hair close to the scalp. She was unhappy about this, but consented. It came off hard and solid like a space helmet and I tossed it on the fire where it spat and crackled furiously, " Sorry Buddha! " I would have to bring delousing lotion tomorrow, meanwhile I put the cloche back on. It would keep her warm.

With Miss Fallows' permission I went upstairs in search of clean clothes. She herself, had not been up for years, and there, shades of Arthur Negus, was a Victoriana paradise. Surely, under that thick coating of dust was Chippendale? Under that grime, Sevres porcelain? In the wardrobes, I found garments which could have graced the Victoria and Albert Museum; in the drawers, hand-embroidered underwear, yellow with age. Rich tapestries hung, rotten to the touch, a world of treasures long abandoned. Fascinated, I wandered into what must have been a box room, an aloof rocking horse and grimy, wax-faced dolls stared back at me. An old stamp album, opened at random, displayed a penny-black. In a corner, excellent pewter and lustre-wear lay cluttered together, and the bright blue and orange of old Staffordshire china defied the dust.

Recalling my duties, I hurried back to a bedroom, collected a few of the most suitable garments and returned below stairs. While dressing Miss Fallow, I told her of the treasure trove that I suspected she had and warned her to let no unauthorised person have access to it. I could see a nimble mind at work under that cloche hat. She was far from senile. If things were arranged properly she could afford to spend the rest of her life in comfort.

By the time I left, I was in no little discomfort. Sternly, I told myself it was psychological, but when slowing down in heavy traffic, I caught a glimpse of black specks playing hop-scotch on my legs. I found it difficult to concentrate on my driving and got several ' V ' signs from lorry drivers. (I am not quite sure of the meaning, but I am certain it is derogatory!) Purposefully, I made for home. Once there, I ran the bath, added disinfectant and got in with my clothes on. When I set off again in fresh uniform I was alarmingly late, but I had taken the precaution of notifying the establishment and extracting from them a promise for immediate action.

When I reached Mrs. Tibbs, she was vigorously wielding a wooden back-scratcher. Outside in the yard, her home help was shaking her bloomers. We compared notes: she was revealed as Miss Fallows' " lady in green."

I finally arrived home with an ominous crawling sensation on the back of my neck and my husband's investigation found several great grey grandfather " bogies," (or were they grand-mothers and still productive?) Head lice have chameleon qualities and change colour to blend with the hair of their host, but obviously these had not had time to adapt (or else the cares of the day had added to the grey hairs I had already lamented!) My husband made a further painstaking and lucrative search of my head and then we all anointed ourselves with " bogey " deterent. It had to stay on for twenty-four hours, and tomor-row, his workmates, the childrens' schoolmates and my patients, would recognise the obnoxious effluvia. It was not the first time and they would all keep their distance.

That night, I was disturbed by an unusual hump under the bedclothes. It was my husband anxiously searching his person

16

with a torch. We spent the rest of the night flea hunting. I bet Buddha never had fleas! By morning he had lost himself a convert.

The children went to school bearing flea bites on their necks, and at nine o'clock promptly and in a truculent mood, I 'phoned the establishment. The condescending young man who answered said he himself had visited the lady in question, had found nothing amiss and on examining her bed, the obvious source of contamination, had found it to be unblemished. I must, he said, be collecting the parasites elsewhere and his tone suggested that I might be breeding them myself. Adroitly, before I could retaliate he rang off. Furiously, I leapt into the car and drove like Jehu to his department.

Poor chap, I obviously shocked his sensitivity by confronting him so precipitously in the flesh, and what flesh! I am one of those unfortunates who blossom forth in weals and bumps at the bite of a flea and my hair hung lank, greasy and odoriferous. Vehemently, I demanded he should accompany me to Miss Fallows and with bad grace he did so. He watched while I dressed her legs and of evidence there was plenty, in fact the creatures appeared to have propagated overnight. Then he kindly suggested to her that she should be admitted to a geriatric ward for a few days while her room was fumigated. In front of her I mentioned the relics above stairs and asked that her interests should be safeguarded. This appeared to be right up his street and he thawed visibly. He had, he said, a considerable knowledge of antiques.

While they were debating, I made a cursory search of the bed: he was right there, none of the telltale marks which always denote the presence of fleas! It was quite incredible. We discussed it on the way back, but were unable to solve the enigma and parted amicably, I noted with satisfaction that he was surreptitiously scratching under his armpit.

The following evening I called to see Miss Fallows in the geriatric ward where she had been installed. She had, I felt, had a raw deal which she had accepted graciously and when she came out of hospital she would again be my responsibility. She sat propped up in bed wearing a capelline bandage on her head and was delighted to see me. I had taken her a boudoir cap, a Christmas gift of several years past, frilled and beribboned and

17

definitely not me. On Miss Fallows it gave her an air of aristocracy. Everyone, she said, had been so kind: there was the possibility her house might be bought and converted into flats, with herself on the ground floor, or else in a small council flat.

She was exhilarated by the prospect of financial improvements and by the interest which had been taken in her. " But it does seem strange," she said, " sleeping here. I've always spent the night in my old chair, dear. Better for my chest, you know. Haven't slept in a bed for years! "

*　*　*

I always enjoyed my sessions with Mr. Pugh: he was a little dried up old man who had lost a leg when being run over by a tram and the stump was now giving him trouble. He lived alone in a tiny house in the shadow of the ' Pepperbox,' the parish church, so called because of its tower which was shaped like a pepperpot. I had attended the homely little church at the age of four, and although loathing Sunday School, I enjoyed day school and the company of small associates. There was Flossie and there was Rose: how I envied them their pretty names, after over fifty years we are still friends. We children took part in all the old church customs. On Ascension Day, all the school joined hands to encircle the church — there weren't really enough of us and it nearly pulled our arms out. Breathlessly, we danced round it singing " Fight the good fight "; it was known as " clipping the church." Each of the stained glass windows had a replica of the church incorporated into the background, and still bears evidence of the lovely old pepperpot tower which has since been pulled down and replaced by a modern one, thereby destroying the whole character.

Before his encounter with the tram, Mr. Pugh told me he had been a " night sile mon." I, too, had reason to remember night soil, and when we reminisced together I was again transported back to childhood, peeping through my bedroom window to watch a cavalcade of jingling carts pass by. Shadows of the men and horses, thrown by the swinging lanterns, loomed sinister and fearsome in the dark hours of the night. When I crept chill and trembling back to bed, it was to weave tales of smugglers with " brandy for the parson and baccy for the clerk."

Actually, the cargo in those carts was nothing more than the unwholesome fruit of the town's privys, which was liable to be dumped on any open ground, especially where there was an accommodating hollow, so that great pools of excreta scarred the outlying districts. From time to time some inebriate, heading for home across the fields, would stumble into the mire and the night would be rent with frantic cries: " 'Elp! 'elp! I'm in the shit! " Then men, all dummicked with sleep, would fumble for their trousers and there would be the clatter and hoarse cries of rescuers as they hurried with ropes and planks to drag out the victim, now probably up to his neck in the bog.

We had a privy at the bottom of our garden next to the ash pit, for there were no bins then. Inside the privy was a bench seat with three holes, one large, one medium and one small, suggestive of poppa bear, momma bear and baby bear, but we didn't use it. Father, very go-ahead, had installed a water closet with a large W.C. painted on the door. Complete strangers came for miles just to pull the chain and marvel at the wonder of it all. Father was proud of his loo and spent long periods there with the morning paper, much to the annoyance of mother when she was pipped at the pedestal. Ironically, the undulating field beyond the garden had been commandeered by the night soil men. Father was furious and wrote protesting letters to the council every time the wind blew in our direction.

Once, as a small child, I had clawed my way through our hedge to explore the field. It was a day of green and gold and bumble bees, heaven high a tiny speck that was a lark trilled; on the horizon a minute train chugged along the railway embankment and a distant church clock struck the hour. A little way ahead grew a young hawthorn tree — 'bread and cheese' we called them and ate their tenderest leaves. This one was curiously foreshortened, its branches low to the ground. I looked down. At my feet spread a great brown expanse, the surface crusted smooth and crying out to be run across. I ran and was engulfed in excrement; giant suckers tugged at my feet and my fingers clutched at nothingness. The more I struggled, the deeper I sank. I threshed about abortively. Then suddenly I touched something solid, staunch, immovable, and I clung to it. It was the hawthorn tree. No wonder it looked out of proportion. Two-thirds of its trunk was submerged in mire. I clawed upwards until I reached the lowest branch and was able to drag my way out. As I lay on the bank exuding filth, only the skylark was witness to my plight and I was already planning how to escape detection.

19

A brook ran at the bottom of the field and I lay in it, sullying its clear waters with my abomination until, despite the heat of the day a chill penetrated my bones and then I made my way, bedraggled and still unwholesome, homewards. " Where ever have you been? " cried my poor mother. " In the brook," I truthfully replied, and was speedily dunked in the brown earthenware sink which was conveniently full of hot, soapy water and where I was scrubbed with pink carbolic.

When dad came home, mother cried, " Our Edie's fallen in the brook, just you smell her! You know what that is; if it's seeping in the brook there's no knowing where it will be carried; into the drinking water I shouldn't wonder."

Solemnly and without preamble, father reached for his writing pad. When I told Mr. Pugh of my earlier escapade he reckoned I was lucky to escape. He often wondered. he said, how many small creatures had disappeared without trace.

I met the Dainty's when they were visiting one of my more affluent patients and because I was without a car they insisted on giving me a lift to my next port of call. It was natural that en route they should enthuse on their pet subject, which was the promotion of health foods. They were themselves vegetarians and grew most of their own provisions.

" The only way of ensuring that it's pure," specified Mr Dainty, " is to have your own garden. No fertilizers, no manures, no artificial aids, just God's good earth! "

To this they attributed their well-being. It was refreshing to hear someone boasting of rude health.

Encouraged by my interest, they begged me to see their garden. We would almost pass it anyway and it would have been churlish to refuse after their kindness. They had a comparatively new house, quite close to where our old one had stood, and when I said I had lived there as a child they were delighted by the coincidence. The prolific vegetable garden was worthy of their pride; " No better soil on earth than this," enthused Mr. Dainty, " pure, unadulterated and as God made it."

It was a beautiful day; on the horizon a minute train chugged along the railway embankment and a distant church clock struck the hour. A gnarled hawthorn tree grew near at hand. I patted it affectionately, it was an old friend, for suddenly I knew just where I stood. The years rolled away and looking down I saw, not the flourishing spinach, the fat marrows, the luscious peas and the verdant lettuces, but a great brown expanse, the surface crusted smooth and crying out to be run across.

*　　*　　*

As soon as I had spoken I knew myself to be a spoilsport, a heel of the first water, but what would you have done?

Jeremy was my neighbour's only child. He was an imaginative boy, probably because he was not allowed outside his own garden and consequently spent much time playing on his own. Recently, however, he had basked in unusual popularity. All the local children, it seemed, came to play with him, my daughter included. From my kitchen window I could see them dancing and posturing round an old disused chicken-pen, the only structure in their otherwise uncluttered garden. From time to time they paused simultaneously, knelt on the ground, bowed their heads thrice, and let forth an ear-splitting triumphant whoop. I pondered on the strange activities of youngsters and reminisced on my own cowboy-and-Indian days. My own offspring came home incredibly muddy considering the unusually dry weather, and when I protested she explained that they made " mud pies and things." When I expressed surprise that Jeremy's mother should allow them to play with water, she laughed derisively, " Gosh! She'd never do that! It's Jeremy, he's got magic! "

Jeremy, she explained, had in a dream had a visitation from the spirit of an African rainmaker (I told you he was an imaginative child), the spirit had lingered long enough to initiate him to rain-producing spells, and now Jeremy had only to retire into solitary confinement and mutter incantations while his familiars made ritual dances round his ' temple,' and, hey presto! he emerged triumphant with a jar full of rain. A bit far fetched, I thought, but well, you know what children are.

A few days later, Jeremy's mother came to see me in obvious distress. " It's Jeremy, nurse, I'm so worried. I know the weather's warm, but he's drinking all the time, gallons of water. It's not natural for a child to be so thirsty."

" How do you know he actually drinks it all? " I asked, seeing a glimmer of light.

" Oh, but he does," she replied. " I watch him drink it, every drop, he just keeps coming in for more."

21

Her fears were obvious, her mother was a diabetic and one of the first symptons of the condition is excessive thirst. " Save me a specimen of his urine," I said, " I'll test it for you."

When she brought me the sample the following day nothing abnormal was discovered. I had not expected that there would be, but I promised to repeat the test at regular intervals to reassure her. She was still unconvinced: " Something must cause his thirst," she persisted. " There's a reason for everything. Perhaps he should see the doctor. Do tell me, what would you do about it? "

" I think," I said, already hating myself, " I think I should pull down that old chicken pen."

After the demolition of the chicken pen, Jeremy's talent for witchcraft evaporated and his following with it, so that before long he was playing solo again. Not that he found his own company inadequate; he was a versatile child and had many interests. He pithered about the garden and decided to become a botanist instead of a witch-doctor. Apart from the ban on playing outside his home ground, his parents were indulgent; he had a cat " Tabby," a dog " Spot," (both neutered of course) and four goldfish, " Matthew, Mark, Luke and John." His father studied books on the birds and the bees and fed Jeremy's inquiring mind on carefully chosen extracts. No gooseberry bushes in their garden!

Jeremy's maternal grandmother, a diabetic, was widowed. Three of her four daughters had escaped her via marriage, but Mary, the youngest, dutifully stayed home. She was good natured and gentle, and thirty-one; if she mourned her wasted youth, it was only to herself. Momma had once kept a market stall and had done very well out of it, but her daughters preferred to forget their humble beginnings. Even Jeremy grieved that she was so cultureless. Once, after a day in the country, he explained to her the function of the catkin and how it was that the hazel tree came to have a little nut, but she cackled bawdily; " S'truth! Cost 'ear the lickle nerker? 'Ee'll be a don' an' when it cums ter puttin' a bun in th' oven! "

Jeremy was perplexed. Cooking was not his metier.

One evening a week, the two elder sisters, who were childless, took over to give Mary a night out. She usually reciprocated by sitting in for Jeremy's parents, until it happened that art classes were started at the local night-school, and then, to

22

everyone's surprise, she decided to enrol. Momma took refuge in ridicule: "Yoh mus' be coddin'! Skewl! An' yoh aclimbin' up the bonk o' forty! They'll bost o' loffin'!"

On that first evening Mary got cold feet and nearly funked it; only momma's mockery spurred her on. Her fellow students were a cosmopolitan lot; two arty youths in matching sweaters and trews held hands caressingly, both flaunted pale shoulder length hair and chained medallions. Embarrassed, she looked away, but they were later revealed as husband and wife employing "togetherness." There was a coloured bus-driver still in uniform, a nun, and a group of lively teenagers chattering over a charcoal sketch and two housewives, matronly and reassuring, cag-magged together. Mary stood hesitantly at the art teacher's desk as he bent over the register and he looked up inquiringly; in that moment their two lives fell into one predestinated pattern. After class, he escorted her home, and by the time they got there, they knew all that was important about each other.

William was thirty-six and unattached. Neither of them had time to waste, marriage was a foregone conclusion, and as they parted on the porch in the gathering dusk the bobowlers blundered into them unnoticed. Until Mary had got into the house she had completely forgotten momma! Her state of grace betrayed her, for momma was immediately susceptible to anything which might affect herself and Mary was too naive to resort to subterfuge. Cocooned in wonder, she was impervious to derision and disbelief. Momma withdrew her taunts, frustrated and franzied.

For days the family remained stunned. Momma was the first to recover and shrewdly reviewed the situation. She had now met William and recognised in him a supervisory force which was not her "barrer." She visualised him superintending her diet; She'd be "clammed to jeth." He might even seek to restrict the "drap of ode crater" with which she was wont to lace her tea, she couldn't abide bossy blokes!

With a blackcountry woman's talent for converting unavoidable misfortune into something advantageous, she began plotting her future prospects. After much cogitation she reckoned that if she let William and Mary rent her house and honoured each of her daughters with her presence for three months annually, she would both supplement her income and also have a finger in everyone's pie, a joy she had long yearned for

While the family were still stupefied, she called a conclave, and informed them of her plans. They were dumbstruck at this fresh disaster. "Doh be mumchance!" she admonished, misinterpreting their concern, "I shore werrit, theer's plenty a goo in th' ode gel yet!" That was precisely what they had feared.

Jeremy alone rejoiced. His new uncle had embellished his scrap book with fine illustrations of his botanical specimens and had promised he should participate in the nuptials as a page boy. His cup was brimming over.

The great day dawned and the respective families, resplendent in festive attire, flanked the aisle. Momma, crammed into new corsets, longed for release. Through the stained glass windows, the sun blessed William and Mary with a rosy glow, and Jeremy, sailor-suited and anticipatory, waited behind them. This was the first homo-sapien union of his experience! It was a moving ceremony, and when it was over momentary silence filled the little church. Jeremy could contain himself no longer; into the hushed solemnity rose his clear treble. "Uncle! Are you going to give Auntie your pollen now or when we get home?"

* * *

District nursing is more accommodating for a married nurse with a family and working from home, and I naturally traded under my married name which was Cockerill. I found it rather an amusing name, the sort you could dine out on, but my sister-in-law had other views. As a child, she said, she had suffered such distress and embarrassment because of it, that when we had children she thought we should change it to protect them.

The whole idea was ludicrous, but the seed was sown. How intriguing to choose a new name! I thought longingly of Cholmondely and St. John, pronounced Sinjun, and sat up nights reading the telephone directory.

I had almost forgotten the subject when an older colleague whose opinion I valued highly said, "For heaven's sake, Cocky, why don't you change your name?" ("Cocky" was my kennel name and still is, though it belies my shy and unassuming nature). The topic was revived, I even made inquiries as to how it was done. Apparently, you can just adopt a name, and state that you wish to be known by it. It's as simple as that.

24

Alternatively, it can be done the hard way by enlisting the services of a solicitor who, after participating in devious spells known only to solicitors, announces your new moniker in the London Gazette and, on receipt of fifteen quid, hands you your deed poll. The fifteen pounds covered the four of us; cheap at half the price.

When I approached my husband about it, surprise surprise! he raised no objections, but stipulated that if it was done, it must be legally and I must do the doing.

My father-in-law was amused, but said he certainly did not mind. My own family were indifferent; it only confirmed what they had always suspected — that I had a tile loose.

Faced with no opposition, I lost interest until one day when overtaking my daughter on her way home from school I saw that she was followed by a taunting group of boys. Their licentiousness is best not repeated and my ire soon dispersed them, but when questioned she admitted tearfully that it was a common occurrence.

I was inflamed in defence of my young. Soon, she was due to move to a new school, she should not go as a Cockerill, something must be done, ack dum! While the mood was on me, I hastened to 'phone my father's solicitor and make an appointment for the following day.

That night I lay sleepless, for by morning we had to have a new name. Despite my earlier aspirations I reckoned that one similar to our own would be less complicating and much easier to adopt. Out of the darkness came inspiration, Cotterill! Only two letters needed to be changed. People might even be led to believe that the other was an error on their part!

What was more important, it was a beloved name to perpetuate, a cherished family name, reincarnated from the past.

Once more I was at Cotterill's farm, the ancient home of my father, and once for a short period of childhood, my home, too. Memories overwhelmed me. Rover, the big black yard-dog, delicately collecting eggs, warm from the nest. He had no objection to my sharing his kennel, but the eggs he ate himself. Uncle Sim, with his tight curly hair, slicing mangel-wurzel and surreptitiously slipping me a slice when mother was not looking. Sim, what a grand old family name, smacking of the good earth and medieval husbandry. Sim, I rolled it round my tongue and loved the flavour of it.

I recalled family Christmas's, the roast turning endlessly on the spit. Carrots and peas on willow-pattern plates. Small boys in knicker-bocker suits, hair smarmed back and tongues in cheeks. Little girls with dodging on their drawers and fluted wings of broderie anglaise sprouting from the shoulders of their starched white pinnys. Carols in the parlour, with the harsh, horse-hair sofa scratching the back of our bare legs; the aunts and uncles glorying in their magnificent voices. Only Uncle George was inharmonious; they shushed him and told him he would put a brass band out.

Then there was Big Jack with his powerful rendering of "Danny Boy." Many years later I was to hear him sing the haunting lament for the last time, on the day of his death as he lay in the old fourposter in which they had all been born. This time it was in a tiny little voice, but every note was true.

The wonderful old farm was mentioned in local history books and bore the date 1638. Her walls were staunch and her doors of heavy oak. "It would make a good council estate," said councillors invested with temporary power.

"It would make a good museum," suggested another tentatively.

"Who would ever want a museum!" they scoffed. They were hard-headed men with an eye to the future.

The farm was demolished, not without dignity, for the great twisted chimneys defied and broke the tackle brought for their destruction. Now the name at least should be ours.

Having made up my mind, I consulted my husband.

Waiting in the solicitor's anteroom, I wondered if it would work. I once knew a butcher named Death, who changed it to De-Ath, but everyone still called him Death. I felt rather foolish too; it seemed such a silly thing to have come about.

The solicitor was a kindly man, acclaimed by my father, and highly esteemed by many. His death has since depleted us all. His avuncular approach invited confidence and I waxed eloquent on the indignity of such a name as ours, the obscenities into which it could be translated by rude little boys, and the utter degradation of it all.

He heard me out and when I had exhausted myself, he still sat regarding me across his desk with a quizzical smile.

Then I remembered. His name was Cox.

*   *   *

I really did have an Aunt Fanny and I loved her dearly. She died when I was eleven years old, but by then she had coloured my whole life.

I knew myself to be a very wicked child. At a tender age I boasted the pet name of " Serpent," but Aunt Fanny believed I was good, and with her I was; I could not bear to disenchant her. My poor mother, driven to distraction by my contrariness, could never convince her of my Jekyll and Hyde disposition; it was pointless to be good with mother anyway, since she already knew the worst.

My aunt and uncle kept a dairy and, amongst other things, Aunt Fanny taught me how to make cream cheese from milk which had ' turned,' and how to ensure that sterilized milk had been effectively processed. For the latter, one upended the bottle and struck it smartly on the base with a clenched fist; if it responded with a sharp click all was well, but if not, it must be returned for resterilizing.

She also taught me how to make beds. The one she and my uncle slept in was a huge four-poster with a canopy, in it my grandparents had lain and begotten their brood. It was draped with pink curtains decorated with bobbles and when it was made we always wound a little gilt musical clock which rewarded us with its tinkling tune. She mourned sadly over the bunion which I had already developed, and soothed the aching joint by painting it with iodine. Once, during Lent, she proposed that I should give up sugar in tea. I was very willing, for her I would have given it up for life, which indeed I did; when Easter dawned I no longer liked it, to the chagrin of mother who accused me of being a " faddy." I was also obstinate and forever my tea remained unsweetened. It proved to be an asset during the years of rationing and a safeguard against the accumulation of adipose tissue.

I harboured a fond nostalgia for the district of those idyllic childhood memories and when, purely by coincidence it became mine for over twenty-three years, I carried the affection with me.

District nursing is like no other, since one is admitted to the patient's innermost sanctum and accepted as one of the family. I was paid fifteen pounds a month (a princely sum to one who had started at fifteen pounds a year), but it was nine years before I had saved the deposit for a car. Uniform was not provided for two years and I wore my old hospital gear with the long sleeves and starched detachable cuffs. Children rushed ahead of me crying their shrill warnings, " Aye up! 'Ere comes the nus with collars on 'er risses! " and vied with each other for the honour of carrying my little black bag, which was really navy blue.

On foot I was most vulnerable, and it was taken for granted that I would deal with any crisis from wife beatings to children locked in lavatories. Once, a harassed and expectant father, searching for a midwife called hopefully: " Aye! bin yo' a pregnant nus? "

When the ' Scheme ' broke out, salaries were increased and more nurses enlisted. Later, when we were beginning to settle down, it was decided by the powers that be that we should each in turn be sent away on a refresher course.

We were all a bit long in the tooth and it was years since we had finished training, but we none of us wanted to go. It was not optional and I was chosen as the first victim. I made vain protests and bleated feebly about having to leave my family (They, ungrateful wretches, were delighted and planning all they would do in my absence). Brochures arrived and a railway permit from Birmingham to London finalised the arrangements. I was instructed to take a set of uniform, as the course would include one hospital visit. I was horrified, having taken for granted that uniform would be the order of the day. If it was to be worn only once, what would I wear the rest of the time?

I hate buying new clothes, but on my day off I planned a shopping expedition. Threatened by my family not to come back with navy blue, for which I have an affinity, I settled for a little grey suit which buttoned up to a round collarless neck. It was crying out for a white blouse to complete it, so I invaded the girls' department of a well-known chain store and invested in two very neat ones with Peter Pan collars. On my return, they would supplement my younger daughter's school uniform.

For days preceding my departure I rushed around demented, laying in food stocks as if for a seige, cleaning, washing, and pinning notices on doors.

Have you turned the hot water off?
Have you left the gas on?
Don't forget to feed the fish.

28

Please water my plants.
Is the cat shut in a bedroom?
Go back and have another look.
Stop. Have you got your key?

At last the time came; the family saw me off at Birmingham and gave me alarming lists from which to choose their ' coming home ' presents. Anything, they assured me, was available in London. I felt apprehensive on the journey and kept remembering things I had hitherto forgotten. I wondered if they would find the chip-pan which I had hidden under a bed. If they did, they would surely set themselves on fire before my return.

My new quarters were near Marble Arch, but I have no bump of locality and following my husband's instructions and feeling very extravagant, I took a taxi. On arrival, I was shown to my room which was small and spartan, with a chair, a tallboy and a narrow bed. I was thankful to have it to myself. There was just time to change before the supper gong, when district nurses of all shapes and sizes swarmed into the dining room. Most were soberly garbed; those who were not stuck out like sore fingers and I viewed my grey suit and fresh white collar with smug satisfaction. During the meal, we all eyed each other suspiciously and ate in silence, except for a few who recognised each other as past acquaintances and were acclaimed with cries of joy. There was a sprinkling of male nurses, but I had never worked with a male nurse then, and took a dim view of them.

We dined off rather stringy cold ham and limp salad, with custard tart and prunes for afters. When we filed out again we were each handed a round disc, backed with a pin, on which to inscribe our names to wear for identification purposes. Foolishly, I wrote on mine, " I like Ike," and deservedly became mistaken for " I. Likle," degenerating as we became more familiar, to " Likle Tot," (I'm a long five foot seven!)

The girls — we were all " girls " again — who occupied the rooms adjoining mine, ganged up with me and unbidden, came in. Cameron was a dark, dour Scot, but the other, Shingles (and immediately dubbed " Herpes Zoster ") was plump and bouncy with beautiful hair, the colour of ripe manure. Disastrously, she always wore pink. We sat talking shop until midnight when the lights were automatically switched off and we

29

were left to grope our way to bed in the dark. A radiator at the head of my bed gurgled and belched all night. I put my pillow at the foot of the bed and lay the wrong way round, but the rest of the night was sleepless. A gong sounded at six-thirty and at seven an unseen call-girl thundered on all the doors announcing breakfast at seven-thirty.

The tables were laid with small packets of cereal and large packets of all bran, and we lined up at the self service for the second course, which was an egg on a slither of pork luncheon meat.

The first lecture at nine o'clock was committed to introducing the syllabus and was given by the formidable sister-tutor who was in charge of us, and who promptly reduced us to the status of junior probationers. Her name was Miss Collins and so, naturally, to us she became " Lottie." She adjured us to make the most of this wonderful opportunity of learning, and not to waste the taxpayers' money.

The days dragged on; meals followed the same pattern, figs sometimes supplanting the prunes to the discomfort of denture wearers. Most of the lectures were old-hat; those on new drugs were our greatest need, but with these names were complicated, defying spelling and pronunciation, and our no longer youthful brains found difficulty in assimilating and retaining knowledge. Frantically, we scribbled notes in exercise books in deference to the taxpayers and numbed our earnest bottoms on the slatted seats.

District work involves the heavy lifting of helpless patients. Most of us had been doing this for years in our own peculiar ways with no ill effects: now we were told we had been doing it all wrong and at great risk to ourselves. We were taught anew how to lift in pairs (no use protesting that we all travelled alone and must needs manage unaided, Lottie withered us with a glance). Awkwardly, we obeyed instructions, heaving each other around in alien and most inelegant postures. Several nurses, who had been hoisting heavy patients uneventfully for twenty years or more, pulled muscles, or worse, and hobbled around for the remainder of the course in a crouched position, walking as if with two left legs and with an agonised expression.

Eminent lecturers honoured us, sometimes starting as late as nine o'clock at night in order to fit us in with their busy schedules. There was no free time for shopping or having a meal out, and after supper, long queues formed at the 'phone in the corridor to enquire anxiously about young families left at home.

It was after ten-thirty one night before I achieved my first call home. My younger daughter answered and undiplomatically, I demanded to know why she was still up. She replied indignantly that they were busy decorating (Heavens!) and where was the chip pan? When I asked for father, he was in the bath having covered himself in paint; my elder daughter was out with a new boy friend (instantly rape was uppermost in my mind!); everything else was fine, except the cat was missing and " Bo'sun," my old whippet, was pining and refusing food. O, and grandad had hit his head with the chopper. What on earth were they thinking of, letting grandad loose with a chopper? At this point, and to further demands as to the whereabouts of the chip pan, we were cut off. It was all very disturbing. I wished I hadn't 'phoned and lay awake all night worrying about them.

Entertainment had been arranged for us with a visit to the ballet and a trip to see the Ceremony of the Keys. The Ceremony of the Keys, climatic as the chimes of ten reverberated was most stirring, and the sombre sight of the Traitor's gate alone set me back several centuries. Of the ballet I was not sure, but I was inspired to caricaturise the male dancer on a postcard for the family and to inscribe it:

> " Ballet man so lithe and light,
> Leaping high with all your might,
> Pirouetting in delight,
> Aren't your drawers a triflle tight?
> Don't you think that maybe you
> Could wear a little tu-tu too? "

One day was spent in visiting a modern mental establishment, but there was nothing institutional about it, for none of the staff wore uniform, and the patients wandered about at will. We were divided into individual groups, each of which was provided with an escort. Ours was a most immaculate young man, his suit was Saville Row and his linen exquisite. His hands fascinated me, being beautifully shaped and manicured. However, he was a delightful and attentive escort and charmed us all. The decor and furnishings of the establishment were sumptuous with costly curtains and lush fitted carpets. As our companion said, patients who chose to live in such luxury instead of working for their bread were not so daft after all. We, he insinuated, but with forgiving grace, were the " softies."

Occasionally, we met up with the other groups for discussion. The patients were allowed to join in; one moon-faced woman with haywire hair came to us each in turn and we spoke soothingly to her, anxious to show compassion. At mid-morning, we were given coffee and biscuits in the dining room where a glamorous female introduced herself as night sister. She explained her many duties and questioned us expertly on ours, and was very interested and most deferential. Altogether, we had a very enjoyable day with an excellent lunch and tea, and then Lottie put in an appearance to round off the day and to thank matron for her hospitality. The moon-faced woman came forward and said it had been a pleasure, and we realised with horror that **she** was the matron. We felt even more foolish when we found later that ' night sister ' was " Pretty Poll, the persistent prostitute," and that our charming escort was a rapist of the worst order. On the way back, when one of our group found her purse was missing with all her cash and return permit, we deemed it wiser to keep quiet and have a whip round for her amongst ourselves.

The refresher course was due to finish on Saturday at twelve-thirty, the forenoon being occupied with a rounding-off session with Lottie. There was a general panic to inquire about trains, when someone remembered that London shops are closed on Saturday afternoons. No last minute chance of a shopping spree! I decided to get the first possible train, but not to forewarn the folk back home; then I could get their presents en route in Birmingham, and perhaps pass them off as London bought.

On Friday night, for the first time, we were free at seven-thirty and Cameron and Herpes planned a trip into the wicked city. Herpes had always wanted to visit Dirty Dick's, so we enlisted a taxi and left the rest to the driver. Dicks certainly was dirty! It harboured a motley crew, sailors, bearded Bohemians, elegant ladies and foreign visitors all jostled together. We managed to establish ourselves in a dusty corner draped with cobwebs and Herpes, being the most knowledgeable, volunteered to fetch the drinks.

Now I have nothing against drinking at the right time and place, but I have only to imbibe so much as one intoxicating potion and my nose bleeds fiercely the next day. I cannot imagine why; maybe it's all my Rechabite forbears putting the 'fluence on me! I hastily explained this foible to Herpes and asked her to get me a soft drink that at least looked as though it might be something more interesting. She was away some time, and I don't know what drink she brought me, as she said one of the sailors propping up the bar had advised her. Anyway, it was jolly nice, though surprisingly costly. The place livened up after a bit and we became quite giggly and skittish. We bought three rounds between us and Herpes obligingly fetched them all. I stuck to my original drink to play safe, but after the third I just passed out. Somehow, they got me back in a taxi and, with the co-operation of our contemporaries, into my bed.

I woke the next morning with a thundering headache and a mouth like the bottom of a birdcage. Cameron and Herpes came in to view me and after a conference, decided I could miss breakfast, but must attend Lotties last lecture, as it involved signing the register to ensure no one had escaped early. I struggled into my clothes while they were at breakfast and made an attempt to pack my case, but red-hot fingers of pain probed every crevice of my skull and several times I was violently sick. Cameron and Herpes helped me down to the lecture room, and everyone made room for us to install ourselves on the back row, away from Lottie's eagle eye.

Lottie's lecture was a brief résumé of all that had gone before, dwelling finally on the problem of lifting which we had so lamentably failed to solve. She called up two of the male nurses to demonstrate — their muscles were less vulnerable, and asked for a volunteer to be the patient. There were no offers.

" Come along," she cried. " You at the end of the back row, don't sit skulking there! " There was still no response; Herpes nudged me and dazedly I realised I was the one at the end of the back row. Painfully, with throbbing head, I stumbled forward and up the steps on to the platform. Lottie beckoned me into the chair which stood between the two stalwart male nurses. " Come," she cried, warming to her subject, " Off with your coat! " Briskly, she had my grey jacket unbuttoned and off before I remembered the little white blouse gaping beneath.

Futilely, I tried to pull it together to hide the expanse of bust bodice and bare midriff now exposed to all and sundry. There was a rending sound from under the armpits; miserably I gave up and sat bog eyed and blotto, shamed before them all.

My disgrace was complete, nothing worse could happen to me now.

But it could.

And it did.

Slowly, insidiously, relentlessly, my nose began to bleed.

A doctor is ' called in ' but a district nurse is ' sent for.' By many people she is regarded with an amused tolerance as a homely body not on a par for instance with a bright new probationer nurse. My daughter had just started her training: " O, how nice! " cried an interested patient, " She's going to do proper nursing? "

It is a little disconcerting to be so often asked, " Have you ever worked in a hospital, nurse? " and to be faced with incredulity when admitting to have once been a ward sister. Who ever heard of a ward sister cleaning up a patient who has just left the room in the bed? Or had you been " unfrocked "?

The refresher course had not done much for my ego either; only made me realise what an ignoramus I was, and remember the adage that " The greatest sin is ignorance set in motion." Uneasy at heart, I cadged a " Mims " from the chemist to compare with the notes I had scribbled during the lectures on drugs. I began taking " Honnor Morten " to bed with me. Faced with such opposition, my husband retired with the sulks and a hot water bottle.

I raked out my old hospital lecture books and took them to bed with Honnor. When I opened them it was like a trip into the dark ages.

2.

I had really wanted to be a vet, but having neither the wit nor the where-with-all for the long expensive training, I decided to give the noble profession of nursing the benefit of my dedication. When I was accepted by an orthopaedic hospital about a two hour train journey from home, my parents saw me off with obvious relief and loud exhortations to chastity. It was May the fifteenth, nineteen-thirty-four.

When I arrived at the little wayside station, I was gratified to find the matron's car awaiting me, chauffeured by a likeable chap who explained that he was her general factotum. On the two mile trip along the country lanes he warned me not to expect a repeat performance. It only happened once, he said, for all newcomers, lest the long jaunt to the hospital so deterred them that they turned tail and took the next train home. I also learned that the nearest town was ten miles away and that there were two trains a day; the evening one was an express which deigned to pause briefly, solely for the benefit of the nursing staff. On Sunday and Wednesday afternoons, two coaches conveyed patient's visitors from outlying areas. If you were lucky you could get a lift, but not, of course, a return trip. The hospital itself was only two years old. It consisted of a lovely old Hall, previously occupied by a titled gentleman, and now the nurses' home, and two large pavilions ' North ' and ' South,' on which the wards were situated. A little distance from the pavilions was a large and very modern theatre block.

All this was approached by a long, winding driveway, flanked by colourful rhododendron bushes. On this May morning it looked very beautiful. I was ushered into matron's presence and thanked her for the use of her car. She accepted me graciously, not so the attendant home sister. Hers was the task of kitting me out in uniform and I was, she said, quite the wrong shape. She went to work on me with a tape measure, but dismissed my vital statistics as " two yards of single width." I was not worried, curves were not à la mode.

Something, she added, must be done about my hair; there was too much of it and none must show from under the starched white cap. Fringes, or " bangs " were considered to be ' fast,' and must be pinned back until they had grown. The ankle-length dresses with three deep tucks at the hem were of a harsh blue and white striped material and lined with calico. The long sleeves had six white buttons with button holes from wrist to elbow, the elbow itself bore a seventh button, minus a button hole. This, explained the home sister, was to provide a sharp and painful reminder should any nurse be so injudicious as to lean her elbows on the table.

A dozen starched white aprons were added to the dresses, plus a laundry bag, stiff white cuffs and collars and matching belts. The smallest size in belts was a twenty-six inch. I was twenty-two, and so they swung about my waist like hoops until I learned to bodge holes in their immaculate surface and adjust the studs. The collars were high and rigid, and wore a line of demarcation round the neck, so that when off duty we looked like refugees from a chain gang.

I had already been instructed to bring with me black woollen stockings, flat rubber-heeled ward shoes, a watch with a seconds hand and a pair of blunt-ended scissors. With all my new gear stowed away in the laundry bag, home sister propelled me before her into the dining hall. It was filled with chattering nurses, but simultaneously the prattle ceased and all eyes swivelled towards us. On each of the three large tables was a loaf of bread, a basin of jellied dripping and a bottle of brown sauce. Huge enamel jugs of cocoa completed the repast. Sister introduced me briefly, I was, she instructed, to be taken to my room to unpack, and then at two o'clock I was to report for duty on North pavilion. She handed me over to a pimply nurse with brown smears on her apron, who apparently was to be one of my room mates. " I hope, nurse Jennings," she said pointing to the smears, " that those are nothing more than sauce! " Then she made a dignified exit and nurse Jennings stuck out a tongue at her retreating back.

I was given a chair and a cup of strong, sweet cocoa, but I declined the bread and dripping annointed with sauce, though I later found it to be delectable and do so until this day. Meanwhile, my companions continued to devour it with voracity, their chatter renewed doublefold.

Slowly sipping cocoa, I tried to follow their discourse, but so many words were quite alien to me. Some, I was sure, were not quite nice. I did however make a wonderful discovery; surnames only were used. All my life my christian name had been a pain in the neck, but I was no longer ' our Edie! ' Henceforth I was " Humphries! "

Later, I was to work for years with girls, share their bedrooms, their stockings, their innermost secrets, and part still not knowing their christian names. Some were followed by younger sisters, but even then the custom was adhered to by the sisters themselves. " Big Kelly " and " Little Kelly," " Big Potter " and " Little Potter." The fact that in stature the little ones were bigger than the big ones made no difference. Big, merely meant senior.

Inevitably, two o'clock arrived. Nurse Jennings delivered me to the sister of North pavilion, who directed me to the boys ward. " You had better," she said, " get on with the round."

Boys! I had no brothers, I knew nothing of boys. Apprehensively, I entered the ward. Thirty pairs of eyes viewed me speculatively, seeing fodder for fun! The nearest boy demanded a bottle and immediately all the others took up the call. Relieved, I went in search of bottles, at least this was something I understood. I soon located the kitchen and put on all the available kettles to heat. Searching the cupboards, I found a pile of hot water bottles and was hastily filling them when sister tracked me down. Wordlessly, she took me by the ear and led me to the sluice, pointed to a rack of strange receptacles and bellowed into my now painful ear: " Bottles! " She then pointed to even stranger vessels, " Bedpans! " She indicated a large sink with a hole in the middle over which a lavatory chain was suspended. " You empty them there! " Abruptly, she left me.

The boys were now calling more urgently and they wanted

bedpans, too. Most of them lay recumbent on iron frames, or else were incased in plaster. They were very heavy and awkward to lift. Incredibly, I had reached that stage of my life without ever seeing a male form except statues (and they were always furnished with a leaf). Decorously, I averted my eyes, fumbled under the bed-clothes and pushed the bed pans in, all of course the wrong way round! The results were calamitous. Even with the help of the other nurses, it took hours to clean up the boys and re-adjust them on their splints. Toilet paper was not used in those days, but a horrible hairy stuff called 'tow,' which had afterwards to be burned. The patients happened to be on a course of sulphur tablets as well and the stench was terrible. I was very unpopular and had to spend the whole evening washing out sheets.

I shared a bedroom with four other girls, but I was so tired I hardly noticed them. At six-thirty the following morning I was abruptly roused by night sister stripping the bed (none of us had heard the awakening bell so we all got the same treatment). There was a general scramble to get washed and dressed and in the dining room for seven o'clock. I was warned by my room mates to beware of 'Calamity,' the night sister, who was, so they said, an unholy terror. If you didn't eat all of your breakfast she gave you an aperient. Trembling, I entered the dining room just as the clock struck seven. Night sister, a terrifying spectacle with bright yellow hair was doling out porridge to each newcomer. She handed me a great dollop and I acknowledged it courteously. " Thank you, sister Calamity."

A stunned silence ensued. The other nurses stared fixedly at their porridge but night sister withered me with a searing glare. " Kindly leave the room! " she boomed, and I crept out still carrying my porridge. For the rest of my time there, she ruthlessly persecuted me.

Back on duty, ward sister watched me like a hawk and was just as merciless. First I had to pull out all the beds so that the wardmaid could clean behind them and many were elevated at the foot on heavy iron contraptions, just to bawk me. By the time they were all back in situ, I was quite exhausted. Next, I was commandeered by the senior nurse for bedmaking; she was brisk and Irish and rather faddy about " envelope corners." She left all the lifting to me and I had an awful job to keep up with her.

When we reached a boy who only had both legs splinted and was able to sit up, he complained that his bottom was sore. Senior nurse turned on me as I came up at a trot, panting and flushed. " You! " she cried. " Go and get an airing! " How kind I thought, she really was quite human after all. Gratefully, I went out into the grounds and sat under a tree, cool breezes soothed my fevered brow.

I was amazed when someone came in search of me. How was I to know she meant an air ring?

The off-duty periods consisted of two free hours a day and one free day a fortnight; today was the day on which ward sister made out the rota for the next two weeks. She booked my day off for the following day. I had not dreamed of getting it so soon, but doubtless she had reasons of her own. She sent for me and explained that a day off was always preceded by an evening off-duty to enable nurses within living distance to spend the night at home. I would, therefore, finish duties when the bell rang for second tea. If I were to forgo my tea I would just have time to change out of uniform and reach the station in order to catch the evening train. She seemed very anxious I should get the train. Perhaps she was hoping I would not come back.

Consequently, at five-thirty I hurried to my room, shed my uniform and once again donned mufti. The last day and a half had seemed endless and it was strange to be wearing ordinary clothes again. Then I set off at steady pace for the station. It seemed a very long two miles and the express and I arrived simultaneously. It gave a shrill snort of disgust at having to halt for one solitary passenger and I barely had time to embark before we were on our way.

I had the carriage to myself, and as we sped through the countryside I wondered what sort of a reception I would get at home. They would naturally be taken aback by my premature appearance, but if I did not go it might be as long as a month before I had another day off. Then they would be suspicious, and want to know what I had done with my time and the return fare they had given me. It was all a bit of an anti-climax.

The next stop was at a main line station, and this time the wait was a long one. When I asked a passing porter, he explained that the Scottish express had been delayed and that unless we stayed for it, many of its passengers would miss their connections.

Just then it steamed in at the adjoining platform and there was a general exodus. Porters rushed people and their baggage across to my train, and in the affray, two of them bundled a young man into the carriage with me. He seemed rather reluctant, but they threw his luggage in after him, slammed the door and with a shriek of protest at the delay, the train moved off, bent on making up for lost time.

The young man looked around with obvious dismay and then began to pace the floor in great agitation. He was a very presentable chap, but I mentally gauged the distance between myself and the communication cord. He paused momentarily to ask how long it was before the next stop, and when I told him it was about half an hour he groaned aloud, perspiration beaded his brow. Anxiously, I asked if he was ill and then, continuing his capers, he told me. It was all so simple really; he had boarded the other express hours previously but his compartment had no corridor, neither had this. Could he possibly make use of the window? "Of course!" I cried, turning my back towards him.

Urgently, he made for the opposite door and let down the window. Looking at my end of the carriage it struck me he would be needing very long legs! There was the sound of much scrabbling. He appeared to be climbing on to the seat, and, against the gathering darkness outside, I saw his reflection in my window. He was astride the seats like a Colossus.

After a considerable time he descended, re-arranged himself and in some confusion, thanked me. "Don't worry," I beamed "you don't have to feel embarrassed with me. You see," I added with pride, "I'm a nurse!"

It was now over three weeks since I had been let loose upon the world of nursing. I had not yet had a second day off. When returning from the first, I had boarded the rear portion of the train and for some inexplicable reason (except that I was on it!), this part was later unhitched from its counterpart and taken to a different part of the country, leaving me stranded late at night in alien territory.

When I failed to return to hospital no-one was surprised; they decided I had just dunabunk. Ward sister was elated and night sister justified, but when I returned after midnight with a police escort and we caught her snoozing in the office, her rage knew no bounds! Ward sister, since she couldn't be rid of me, decided that I must be knocked into shape and I suffered considerably in the process.

When I heard on the grapevine that a new probationer was expected, I was much gratified. I should no longer be the lowest form of animal life, but when she arrived she was cute, curvateous and came from Crewe. She had a boy friend and a bicycle, and was able to cycle home on her evenings off, and she committed no foolish faux pas. I was consumed with envy.

June came in on a heatwave, patients shed their coverings and nurses their corsets. Lacking suspenders, we rolled our woollen stockings down to below the knee, securing them with bits of string and thereby inviting varicose veins in later years. Our long skirts hid the sacrilege.

The hospital was an open air institution, but now we went a stage further and pulled the beds out on to the veranda, only for a limited time, however. Twenty minutes on the first day (it hardly seemed worth the bother), and a little longer on each succeeding day until eventually the patients lay exposed to sunlight all day long. Much later, when lectures commenced, I was to learn that this method of sunning was the brain child of a certain Doctor Peabody; all of our treatments were modelled on the lines advocated by Doctor Peabody and Dame Agnes Hunt, an admirable lady of high repute and a friend of our senior surgeon.

For decencies sake the patients wore 'tidies' which were small rectangular pieces worn fig leaf fashion and secured by tapes at each corner, like the lower half of a bikini, only less so. On the womens' wards they were also permitted the dignity of a shapeless sort of brassiere and the elderly patients were allowed to go their own way, but there was no false modesty, only during visiting hours adult patients donned more concealing wear. This long exposure to sunlight is not now approved of, but certainly with the graduated method people acquired an enviable tan and no one ever suffered from sunburn.

It was my special responsibility, allied with bottles and bedpans, to see that the boys' tidies were clean and in situ. I was still disconcerted by this bit of male anatomy and never knew what to call it. The boys had no such problem and enjoyed my confusion. If I had to refer to it, it was the 'thing'

I had so far escaped our senior surgeon, a non-resident commonly known as " T' ogre." T' ogre was reputed to arrive

41

unheralded and strike like lightning, leaving the equivalent destruction in his wake. Sisters had hysterics, patients wept, student nurses went home to mother and even Jennings had been known to miss her lunch. Sister herself gave me the drill so that there could be no mistake; if ever the great man ever arrived when I was on duty, I was to make myself scarce. I could 'phone all the other wards to apprise them of his presence, but then I was to shut myself in the sluice until I was told it was safe to come out. I needed no second bidding.

One hot afternoon I laboured alone with the bedpans. Sister was off duty, the other nurses had gone off to first tea, staff nurse had disappeared on some secret mission of her own. A low warning whistle from the boys alerted me and I looked up to see a shining limousine glide to a halt at the steps leading to the ward. A short, stocky, florid faced man alighted, and scaled the steps with unlikely speed, and with horror, I knew it must be T' ogre.

" I'll do a round! " he boomed. I made to escape, bleating something about staff nurse, but he had me by the arm.

" You'll do! " he barked, pushing me before him.

At each bed he paused, testing extensions, flexing groin-straps, sniffing at plasters and his comments were caustic.

We came to a boy who for some reason was not so brown as the others. T' ogre pointed at him accusingly.

" Has that boy had his Peabody sunning? " he demanded.

I stared open mouthed and wrathfully he repeated the question. " Has that boy had his Peabody sunning? "

Suddenly, a great light dawned. Of course, how simple! So that was what they called it!

" Oh no! " I replied a little reproachfully. " He's been sunned everywhere else but he wore a tidy over his peabody."

Matron abhorred smoking and forbade it amongst the probationers. I had long been an offender, for those of us who made the journey to school by train enlivened the tedious trip with " de Reske " minors, in a pale green oval tin, and paid for with bus fares accumulated by trudging the two miles between school and the station. Scorning the conventional carriage seats, we lounged on the luggage racks puffing away like addicts in an opium den.

Seasoned travellers gave us a wide berth, and walking home from the station, I sucked peppermints, lest father, a non-smoker, snould detect the odour. Sometimes he complained of it in my hair, but attributed it to fellow passengers and advised me to travel in a non-smoker.

Now that the habit was forbidden it became a must for all of us, but matron soon got wind of the wicked weed and tracked down offenders ruthlessly.

Burning buckets of tow after the bed-pan round was the obnoxious job of the junior probationers, but it was eagerly sought after by the seniors as an opportunity for a smoking session in the stoke hole. The hall boasted a flat roof surrounded by battlements; our quarters, previously the servants, were on the top floor and the row of six lavatories at the end of the corridor had skylights opening out on to the roof. Anyone needing the loo for a legitimate purpose was invariably foiled by a row of nurses solemnly standing on the seats with their heads through the skylights, puffing away with great concentration.

In summer, the flat roof was a favourite place for sunbathing off duty. It was made accessible by means of a small winding stairway and it was a ludicrous sight to see a row of heads protruding at roof level, all smoking away like decapitated human chimneys.

Many matrons may be female automatons, but ours was just and kind, and really had our welfare at heart. Anyone could take their problems to her. They might be reprimanded, but never condemned. She made a home of the hospital and many of the younger patients remembered no other. One tiny child was encased in plaster because her bones were so brittle, they fractured at a touch; just by moving her own arm she could break it. But she was a merry child and had known no other life, for she was only two weeks old when she was admitted. Last time I saw her, she was still there, but grown into womanhood.

A beautiful boy of four with golden curls and cherubic face hurtled round the wards, sure of a welcome everywhere. His legs ended just below the knee and his feet stuck out like frogmen's flippers. His short arms terminated into a thumb and forefinger but he had an inquiring mind and one day, when sitting on night sister's lap, he looked up into her face; " Tister," he asked, " does all ladies wear pincushions underneath their aprons? "

Neither of these children had ever been acknowledged or

visited by any of their families, but we were their family and they grew up assured of affection. Most of the patients, however, had devoted relatives who mourned their long absence from home, but happiness is an attitude of mind, and few patients were unhappy.

Many of the children were polio victims, their flaccid limbs were useless, but once immersed in a tank of water, or with their legs encased in walking calipers, they managed to get around under their own steam. Everyone had something; diseased hips and spines and knees; congenital deformities; or maybe limbs missing altogether, yet no one saw themselves as abnormal: abnormal ones were those who had nothing wrong!

During off duty on fine days, we took the children out with us, pushing spinal carriages down country lanes, wearing our long hooded cloaks lined with red. Matron only allowed us to wear uniform in the vicinity of the hospital, for she reminded us that we were still untrained and if called on to deal with an accident or emergency, we might do more harm than good. Many of us would have stayed on, probationers growing older, but matron was adamant. After the stipulated two years, she ousted us like fledglings from the nest to do our general training. Only sisters and staff nurses were allowed to make a niche for themselves.

For a long time it seemed that I was general dogsbody on the boys ward. They were an unruly lot and mischievous to the extreme . When they were at last bedded down and all the sisters went to supper, the staff would congregate in the linen room to fast off corn flakes laced with the top off the milk and egg and chips, hurriedly prepared in the kitchen. But, as a junior pro., I was despatched to the ward to keep cave and to control the boys. Strangely enough, I found this no problem once I took on the role of story teller, and providing I kept going, the boys fiercely disciplined each other.

Every evening, I would crouch on a stool in the centre of the darkening ward narrating an endless serial story made up as I went along. Each episode terminated with the supper bell and was recommenced the following night. The hero was an ingenious polio boy known as Harry Stotle, his cunning was such that he constantly outwitted staff nurses, sisters and visiting consultants, and in this way he was aided and abetted by a one legged crony called Hopper. Hopper's remaining appendage was of such strength and resilience that he was able to leap incredible distances, always bearing Harry with him. The couple led a hazardous existence, but with Hopper's projectile limb and Harry's know-how, nothing was impossible!

Wallybags was the most colourful character in the whole establishment. She was an Irish nurse of indeterminate age with fine dark eyes and a caustic humour. I was flattered when she elected to accompany me home when our days off coincided, but Wally was a staunch Royalist, and it was the day on which the Duke of Kent was to make the Princess Marina his Duchess. With all the world to choose from, they had elected to honeymoon in Dudley, at Himley Hall! When her day off was unavoidably cancelled, Wally was inconsolable. " Be japers, now oi'll niver see herself," she keened. Ironically, I had no wish to; I was going through an anti-royalist patch. Anyway, I had little time to traipse around gawping at the nobility.

As usual, the women patients had given me a long list of shopping to do for them. Many of the articles were unobtainable locally, so I had to go into the town after all.

The buses were full, so I had to walk, and when I got there I found the main road was blocked with sightseers lining the route of the royal procession. I tried to push my way through the mass but some folks were very truculent. I lost a shoe, had my bunion trampled on and my beret got pushed over one eye. Then a great swopson of a woman bunted me on the nose and it began to bleed furiously. My handkerchief had been lost in the mêlée.

As a cavalcade of cars came into view, the crowd surged forward bearing me with it. Dishevelled and bloody, I stumbled forward, falling with the flat of my hands onto the bonnet of a slow moving limousine — only a policeman tugging at my coat saved me from the sacred wheels. The inside of the car was illuminated, and as it passed I saw, like a flashlight photograph, two Olympian beings, beautiful beyond description. The lady wore a little pillbox hat and was attired in the Marina green which she so favoured. As the vehicle bore her away, she turned and gave me her sad, sweet, lopsided smile and I was her fan for life.

When at last I graduated to the theatre block, I felt I had really got somewhere. Close proximity with T' Ogre was rather daunting, for he began to call me " the long one " and took a disturbing interest in my bunion. Before operating, he always took a bath and donned clean white trousers, white singlet and long white boots. The overall gown, gloves, skull cap and mask were, of course, taken from a sterilised drum in the theatre itself, together with a pair of long, cheadle forceps. It became my responsibility to prepare his bath and see that his gear was airing on the radiator; also that a bottle of concentrated orange juice was at hand, together with a syphon of soda water. He never drank water, maintaining that it " rotted the guts " and always diluted his fruit drink with soda water. It made a refreshing beverage, for operating theatres are hot and thirsty places and normally it was kept under lock and key, otherwise pilferers filched the orange juice, sacrilegiously adding water to hide the bottle to hide the theft.

Fear of infection to the patient was always the bogey that dogged our heels. Antibiotics were still a thing of the future, and scrupulous care in sterilization was taken; tetanus spores we were told, could withstand anything less than twenty minutes boiling. It goes well for the drill that during my two years there I remember no outbreak of infection, other than the inevitable childish ailments, and there were no deaths.

No credit due to me! On my first day in the theatre I had been filled with enthusiasm and watched avidly as T' ogre made expert slashes with his scalpel, meanwhile concocting in my mind dramatic reports for my next epistle home. I could hear mother boasting to the aunts; " Our Edie's operating now!" Suddenly T' ogre recalled me: " Mop! " he bellucked and I darted into the corridor to the broom cupboard and was back in a flash with a mop. Gowned anonymous figures barred my re-entrance, scandalised eyes condemned me. Through the port hole windows, I could see another, mopping the great man's brow.

The first amputation that I witnessed was from an advantageous position. I was holding the leg which was to come off. It was a very large leg from a very large lady and when it was finally severed it was suddenly all mine and I nearly overbalanced from the sheer weight of it. I was not quite sure what I should do next. Abruptly, both the leg and I seemed superfluous. Hesitantly, I addressed T' ogre, " Have you finished with it, sir? "

" God Almighty girl! " he bellowed. " What the hell would I do with it? Stuff it? "

" Burn it you fool! " hissed theatre sister from behind her mask, " In the stoke hole! "

I swung round with my arms very full of leg, scattering the theatre staff and blundered through the swing doors. Once in the corridor, I paused for reflection. I must get something to wrap it in. Reverently, I laid it on the floor as though it was still endowed with feeling.

I had never been any good at doing up parcels and a leg is not the easiest of objects to package. I tried to camouflage it with a discarded old sheet but however I wrapped it up, it still looked like a leg in a sheet. I gave up, and changed my theatre get-up for the less glamorous overall which sister had given me for cleaning the theatre floor after operations. When I set off with my gruesome cargo I had to make several detours to avoid meeting people. I felt like a body snatcher and just as guilty. The stoke hole, of course, was situated in the basement. It was darksome and gritty with coke, the furnace had been recently replenished and there was not much room left for the leg. Revealed in the half light with its trappings off, the leg was huge and bloated, but it tapered into a tiny little foot, a dear little foot, no corns, no bunion and surely only size four? What a waste, I mourned, comparing it with my own great clodhoppers.

There is something very personal about a ladies leg; surely it warranted some small obsequial rite? But the idea of the burial service being read over a leg (with the owner as chief mourner) was ludicrous even to me. Bracing myself, I thrust it thigh first into the aperture. Immediately the leg assumed an independent existence and resisted me stubbornly. Desperately we fought together. I pushed it frenziedly, flexing the knee, but when I released my hold it kicked back at me, clout ing me on the nose which, true to form began to bleed. Finally, by taking an unfair advantage with a shovel, I subdued the thing and slammed home the door of the furnace, from where it spat and hissed evil incantations. The unfortunate lady who had nurtured it so long seemed much happier without her leg, but I was never able to look her in the eye again.

My second winter came and snow drifted into the wards. It settled on the mackintosh-covered beds and joyfully the children snowballed each other where they lay. All day long we renewed the hot water bottles round them; there were to be shutters on the wards for next winter, but I should not be there.

The storms worsened, the electricity failed as did the telephones, the roads were impassable to traffic and we were cut off from the rest of the world.

Each morning we got up to dress in the corridor round a solitary candle. Hairdressing was easy, since it was all pushed under our caps anyway. Night nurses were worse off, with long lonely nights and fading torch batteries. Thank goodness for gas cookers.

Food stocks got lower, patients were given priority, and when reduced to the unusual luxury of biscuits, we longed for bread. On the fading radio we heard that the king was sinking fast. Matron thought that the bread might have been left at the station as trains were probably getting through. We volunteered to go after duty and she chose the six hardiest of us. The few male members of the staff were mostly recruited from ex-patients and were disabled in some way; they were not to be told.

After a supper of sorts we set off, intrepid and warmly clad and with large water-proofed laundry bags to sling over our shoulders in anticipation of bread. At first it was fun, but snow-drifts lay deep and treacherous and it was not easy to keep to the road. Clinging together, we floundered through them. Lightning flashes illuminated the sky as telepgraph wires collapsed from the weight of snow.

"When beggars die," I quoted, "there are no comets seen, but the heavens themselves blaze forth the deaths of princes."

It was past midnight when we reached the station, but the bread was there. The old porter made us hot cocoa and told us the king had just died.

On the way back we were sobered and heavy laden; our thoughts turned to the new king. By all accounts he was a bit of a lad. Only I had seen him. When he had opened the New Birmingham-Wolverhampton Road our headmistress had been one of the chosen to dine at the reception given for him and we were given the honour of lining the route at an advantageous spot. Actually, I had been acutely disappointed, he looked small and a little bow-legged to me. Perhaps it was all that horse riding, or maybe the long wait had jaundiced my eye. Some-

48

one in the crowd had cried, " Oh! look at him walking! " as though she had never imagined he would have the use of his appendages.

I embroidered the event for them and glamourised the new king. I did not mention the legs. Anyway, they would not show under all that ermine.

In a few days things began to improve, and soon we were in circulation again. On the day of the old king's funeral we congregated with the patients to listen to it on the old ' steam ' radio. In our mind's eye, the commentator, with dolorous intonation, painted a picture of the pomp, the plumes, the solemnity and the sadness. Sombrely his voice droned on, " With bowed head, following the coffin, walks the new king, the Duke of York on his right."

" What's 'e say? " piped up an old girl in the corner; " The Duke o' York on 'is bike? "

Suddenly winter was gone, spring bloomed in the hedgerows and we intensified our strolls, planning our futures with no inkling of the dark war years ahead.

" Gather ye rosebuds while ye may," time was certainly aflying. Too soon it was May again and my turn to try my wings; now would come the real grind. These two years had only been a preliminary for things to come. The hospital at which I had chosen to train was in a south-east coastal town; my sister taught at a boarding school there and I felt a need to be near someone of my own. Night sister had laid bets that I would not stay the course, but that alone was to stand me in good stead and to goad me on when the going was hard.

All who were off duty accompanied me on my last walk to the station; chatter and hilarity hid our real feelings. Over twenty years later, my daughter was to tread the same road, in fact serve under the same staff nurse; the desire to nurse is infective and already my grand-daughter struts in a miniature uniform and all her dolls are subjected to hospitalisation.

On the platform we clung together unashamedly, but the train was as impatient as ever. Someone jumping up for a last embrace bumped my nose with her head. Streaming blood and tears, I hung out of the carriage window until they had disappeared from view.

I had gathered my rosebuds.

3.

General training, after the easy going predictable routine of orthopaedics, was like a douce of cold water. The hospital itself was an awesome edifice composed of slippery floors and long corridors, supported by winding staircases and voluntary contributions.

The training in voluntary hospitals was considered to be superior by far to that of county council establishments, and we who participated were very proud of the fact. Our existence depended on the goodwill of the community and there was no better basis for this than a satisfied customer.

Annually, when eggs were most prolific, we had a day when townsfolk each contributed one. It was our job to pickle them, and they sustained us throughout the year. Another day, in the right season, was dedicated to donations of Seville oranges, and we suffered biliously from much marmalade making.

Preliminary training schools were unknown and seniority was accorded to first comers, thus I left my old hospital as senior probationer to become again the most junior. The nurse who preceeded me by two weeks had come straight from school. She was delighted by her improved status and meticulously initiated me to my duties, but I was fortunate in that she was only too anxious to save me from the snares into which she herself had fallen. Others were less charitable. Seniors automatically took priority in the dining room and sleeping quarters and we " mucky pros " accepted scanty servings and tepid bathwater as our due. One day we too would be lords of creation.

Once more I found myself frequenting the stoke hole to dispose of human rejects, the aborted twins I never forgot.

The woman who conceived them was a "regular." She would never divulge her method of procuring abortions, but this time the evidence was there in the form of a crochet hook which had got stuck.

The babies were too premature to qualify for a burial service (it was usual to place miscarried infants at the feet of some adult corpse, and I often speculated on the consternation of maiden ladies confronted at the "Last Trump" with a new born babe sharing their coffin!) The disposal of them was left to me and I carried them wrapped in newspaper like a bundle of fish and chips.

All stoke holes are much the same and I sat amongst the dusty jumble of coke and shovels nursing the little rejects on my lap and watering them with tears. Lofty of brow, but minutely developed, they were obviously male; delicate fingers curled like limp petals and on their tiny faces were expressions of primeval wisdom and resignation. As I consigned them to the red hot embers, I was their only mourner.

"Why you mugwump!" scoffed the sister when I returned with red rimmed eyes. "You'll never make a nurse!"

Off duty we organised our own amateur theatrical society, concerts for the patients and the medical staff always went down well. Then there were "open days" and, later in the summer, the carnival, which was well patronised by holiday makers, adding to our funds. We designed and decorated our own vehicle and it was a coveted privilege to be chosen to ride with it in the parade.

There was no ban on smoking except in the wards and dining room; it was an accepted thing so the pleasure was gone and I never smoked again.

Once more, it was the top floor that harboured the nursing staff and the domestic staff too. As junior probationer, I occupied a tiny room next to that of matron's maid, Millie, a belligerent female who regaled her mistress with exaggerated accounts of my misdemeanours. My bed was so narrow that if I wanted to turn over I had to get out first and get in backwards, and even that was not easy since the springs so sagged that my posterior was in constant contact with the floor. Millie complained constantly of my nocturnal creakings and it was almost a relief when I was relegated to night duty.

So many nurses went sick when on night duty that it was customary to keep on indefinitely anyone who did not; consequently I spent nine months of my first year's training on nights. There were no nights off-duty until the end of the stint, when we were awarded one for each month that we had done.

I was feeling apprehensive when I reported for duty on my first night. I was carrying a covered meal on a tray, for there was only one nurse to each ward and no time off before eight thirty the following morning. As I stood to attention at ward sisters desk while she read her report to me I felt very important, for tomorrow morning she would be reading mine. She added several last minute instructions and said there was a pile of mending in the linen cupboard to help me pass the time. She made it sound like a favour.

When the day staff went to their supper at nine o'clock, I was left alone. No, not alone! Belatedly, I remembered the patients. Quickly, I changed into the rubber pumps worn by all the night nurses and made a tour of the ward, settling everyone down for the night. The men were a cheery lot and made my job as easy as possible.

I was just finishing when I got wind of the house surgeon, whose approach was always heralded by the aura of macasser with which he strove to subdue his unruly thatch, and in consequence of which he was popularly known as 'Pong.' I wondered idly what he was doing in the kitchen until I remembered my meal which I had not yet investigated. Urgently, I tracked him down. He was notoriously hungry, and as I anticipated, was foraging for food.

Fortunately, my tray had been pushed out of sight and his search revealed only bread, margerine and cocoa (ward sisters shrewdly locked up their poisons and provisions, and secreted the key about their person). Undaunted by the meagre fare, he toasted think hunks of bread and made cocoa for both of us. Obviously, he was used to fending for himself.

The other commodity for which he craved was an audience on whom to laud the merits of his current girl friend, and we all knew about her to our cost. According to Pong, she was delectably delicious, a real oomph girl with oodles of " It," a topical term for sex, and good connections to boot.

To stake his claim to this paragon he had invested in an

engagement ring and was now beset by demands for the instalments on it. As he was reimbursed with half-a-crown for every post-mortem he performed he carried out as many as possible, ghoulishly waylaying relatives for permission. It was usually granted willingly, since they were mollified by his interest — it was in the cause of science, he assured them. Heart condition was his speciality: he did not add that the heart was his own!

Unfortunately, we had to attend these macabre functions to further our knowledge of anatomy and so, although we had never met his betrothed, she was highly unpopular with us all.

Having satisfied the inner man, he ambled off to bed and sweet dreams. Poor Pong, they were short lived, for it was a night of many admissions and he had to deal with them all. A house surgeon's lot is not a happy one.

Almost immediately night sister arrived to do her round, peruse the report, and read me the riot act. I was, she reminded me severely, very junior to be entrusted with the male surgical ward; matron had only chosen me because of sickness amongst the senior nurses and because she had in mind my two years' orthopaedic experience and inevitable knowledge of night work. Dutifully, I acceded to the honour conferred on me but it was, I knew, a double-edged compliment, for no oomph girl ever did night duty on a male ward! Matron in her wisdom penalised all her charmers to servitude on the female wards.

My ward was the one nearest to the private suites of the mighty and I was to find the proximity most undesirable. To start with matron, whose vacation began on the morrow with an early flight, requested a call at 5 a.m. together with a light breakfast. Since no one so menial as myself could approach her in deshabille, the calling was night sister's lot, but preparation of the breakfast was mine and the responsibility hung heavily upon me.

I was dealing with my first admission when Millie, on her way to bed, arrived with the sacred breakfast tray. She kept bobbing up and down behind the screen with instructions that went in one ear and out the other, so that finally she gave up and went away.

The new patient with whom I was dealing was a very aged, unidentified man who had been found wading out to sea. He had resisted his would-be rescuers and was obviously not responsible for his actions. He had evidence of past strength in his great gaunt frame, but examination revealed a monstrous growth which he must have piteously secreted for a very long time. When I had cleaned him up, night sister came and we fixed him with a drip saline, a sort of inverted thermos flask filled with a solution of salt and glucose and suspended at the head of the bed. It was connected to the patient by a length of rubber tubing and the fluid was regulated to be given by slow drip per rectum.

The next admission was a road casualty who had lost a great deal of blood. A transfusion was imperative, but we had a book containing the particulars of blood donors and by referring to this Pong was able to select a suitable candidate who was roused from his bed by the police and brought to the hospital. The donor lay on a bed alongside the patient but screened from view, and the transfusion was, as always, given direct.

The night, which at nine o'clock had stretched interminably before me, now rushed ahead like an express train down a dark tunnel. I could not keep pace with it. Sister's injunctions jostled for precedence in my head. Soon it would be morning and the busiest time of all.

The first streaks of dawn paled the sky when I remembered my meal, and immediately I was ravenous. I uncovered the tray with gratification; haddock! Already lightly cooked, it made a tempting dish, and a fresh brown egg (no pickled one this), obviously awaited poaching with which to crown it. Crisp rolls, teamed with pats of real butter completed the repast, together with a grapefruit so exquisitively crimped and pared, it seemed a sin to eat it, but I did so without compunction. Bully for cook, she evidently realised night staff needed cosseting!

With renewed vigour I pursued my tasks and was laying out the medicine trolley, " Black Jack " and " White Mary," beloved of all ward sisters, when the house 'phone shattered the peace. It was night sister reminding me that she would be along in a few minutes to collect matron's breakfast. Heavens! I had forgotten! For one awful moment I could not find her tray; it had been pushed away in the corner of the kitchen. What was it Millie had muttered? I wished now that I had listened to her.

I lifted the covers and was astounded to see a revolting heap of spaghetti, congealed like roundworms on a plate. Fancy them giving matron grub like that and look at mine.

Cold water trickled down my spine.

I knew that I *was* looking at it.

When I went on duty the following night, all and sundry knew that I had scoffed matron's breakfast; the juniors commiserated, the seniors crowed (that'll take her down a peg or two!) I just hoped she had a very short memory and a very long holiday. I had managed to evade her before she went.

Ward sister was very snarky; her mind was on other things.. " Your old man," she said (she was always to refer to him as this, as though I had perversely sought him out in the highways and byways just to annoy her!) had been giving a lot of trouble. He had recovered from his dip in the sea sufficiently to pull down his drip saline and make a mess all over her ward. " Her nurses," (I was not " hers " — I was night sister's) had had a very trying day, and now they had to put up bed boards to prevent him from getting out of bed. Everyone knew how she detested bed boards, they made her ward so untidy.

The old man had been identified as a Mr. Clay and had no known relatives. His age was indeterminate, but he was certainly in his nineties. Further, to vexate sister there had been numerous discharges and the equivalent admissions, all for operation on the following day, and therefore still ambulant. It exasperated her to see menfolk littering the ward; she liked them in two neat rows lying to attention with eight inches of the top sheet turned down and the vents in the pillow cases all facing away from the door. The men kept ragged bits of string of the required length under their pillows and measured their bit of sheet before she did her round, bequeathing them when they went home to the newcomers. Not that she would ever give vent to her ire on patients, but they felt the whiplash of her tongue when she berated the nurses.

Five of the new cases had inguinal hernias. I must do their initial preparing for operation and " woe betide if they're not clean shaven." I did take umbrage at this, for I was already reputed to be the slickest, speediest shaver in the business. With " T' Ogre's " high standard behind me, I could be little else; let there be so much as a 5 o'clock shadow on his site of operation and he bellowed for the offender to be brought before him. That was one way of learning. Still, she ranted on, so that it was with great relief that I saw her finally go off duty and flopped down into her chair, only to shoot to attention again as she came darting back, having forgotten to tell me to " do " the bandages, and not to forget the mending I had not done the night before.

" Doing " the bandages was a tedious chore. They were white cotton bandages of a quality that varied according to the current financial status of the hospital funds and they had to be washed, boiled, ironed and wound up with a little rolling machine. They were used repeatedly until they literally fell to pieces. I found them soaking in the sluice, and after a quick rub, put them on to boil. If I got them done in time, one of the patients could roll them for me in the morning. I would get someone else to make the swabs for the " drums," as I always hated that job, because the cotton wool went up my nose. Packing the drums was a must for night nurses; they had to be filled with clean dressings and ready for the porter when he came on duty. He took them to the sterilising room where they were dealt with and returned in time for the day staff to do the mornings dressings. There was never enough cotton wool, but we used to open the new rolls and spread them over the radiators before packing — the warmth made them increase to twice their bulk.

Mr. Clay had been given medication but it had not taken much effect, and when I went into the ward he was rattling the boards which gave his bed a coffin-like appearance, and making hoarse animal noises. I hoped he was not going to keep that up all night. The inguinal hernia blokes, drawn together by a comman ailment, had formed a little clique and were nattering like women; anyone would think it was a pub. I would soon put a stop to that. I would shave them all now! Some of sister's bad temper had rubbed off on me. I rushed down the ward with screens and necessary equipment and got on with the job, anxious to finish before night sister put in an appearance. The hernias fell silent and eyed each other apprehensively.

I suppose to be so intimately attacked by a crazy teenage female with a cut-throat razor can be a little off-putting; they lay petrified and unresistant. I had shed all my false modesty in the past two years and worked with speed and precision. It was like a sheep shearing. Before night sister arrived, everything was cleared away and the ward lights dimmed, only a row of little humps under the bed-clothes suggested my victims were anxiously investigating to see if I had done them a mischief.

56

The recipient of last night's transfusion was so improved that I did not recognise him until he greeted me like an old friend, but Daddy Clay was a thorn in the flesh. Pong wrote him up for further medication, but it was no more effective than the first; his carcinoma and incontinence were very offensive, and when I tried to clean and change him, he resisted violently, and sought to cover the foul growth as though to him it was a shameful thing. I made some gruel and fed him from a spoon; he pursed his lips and supped it like a baby, and clung to me with a fierce grip lest I should go with it unfinished. After that, he began a slow rhythmic motion as though his boarded bed was a boat he was rowing through a heavy sea. Once he ceased, only to peer into the shadows like some pale ghost before cupping his hands to his mouth and letting out a long " Halloo! " which pierced the night like a clarion call, startling all the men and rousing the assistant matron from her bed. " Really nurse! " she snapped, " can't you manage your ward better than this? "

I put a light over the old man's bed and the small ward table and chair beside it, and then I took my various chores and charts and did them beside him. Each time he raised his hands to repeat the hallooing I shushed him severely, but the patients were resigned to a sleepless night and tossed relentlessly. I felt sorry for the operation cases; they would be lying awake dreading their ordeal. It would soon be morning, and there was so much to remember. I must not forget their early morning specimens. All the pre-operative men must have their urine tested and it must be the first they passed in the morning.

I had begun the report, when out of the corner of my eye I saw one of the hernias slip out of his bed and make for the toilet. My specimen! I dashed in after him. " Wait! Please wait! " I cried urgently. " I want a specimen from you." He paused apprehensively, wondering what fresh indignity was to be committed on him.

" I want a specimen of your urine." I explained patiently. He still looked nonplussed. A row of specimen glasses stood waiting up on the shelf and I pointed to them. " I want you to pass water into one of those."

" What! " he cried aghast. " From 'ere! "

Daddy Clay clung tenaciously to his miserable life, to the

great vexation of ward sister. He appeared to have outlived his contemporaries and no relatives came forward. Geriatric institutions would have accepted him but not his malignant tumour, and as soon as the side ward became empty, sister had him moved in there. At least her ward was tidier without him, though it had the disadvantage of bringing him within range of her office. She complained bitterly of the abnuxious affluvia and burned foul smelling cones to eradicate it; of the two I preferred Daddy Clay. He still kept up his strange hallooing and indefatiguably rowed his boarded bed. Drugs had little effect on him, and his hoarse cries could be heard all over the hospital. " Old stinker " was decried by all. The night staff's quarters were situated just above the ward and intermingled with the clatter of bedpans or the cag-mag of visitors, his halloos haunted us all day, not that we could sleep in any case. The staff linen room was at the end of our corridor and the assistant matron was constantly to-ing and fro-ing and rustling laundry paper. Also, we were roused to attend lectures, and Millie, who came to call us, plodding along on her great splod feet, usually woke the wrong people anyway!

The holiday season was in full swing bringing with it the usual spate of casualties, and the pier more than anything contributed to these. There was the man who dived off it into two feet of sea and broke his neck; another, tempted by the " try your strength " contraption fractured his spine, and then there was the boy who was doing nothing in partciular except watching the fisherman and got a fish hook in his face. Fish hooks were a common casualty in outpatients and were easily removed by simply cutting off the line and pushing the hook itself through, like a sewing needle, to a different point of exit. The boy's father, however, had persistently tried to pull out the hook from the point of entrance, causing severe laceration and resulting in infection. The boy was now critically ill with cellulitis of face. The cruel barb, of course, prevents the hook from being pulled back. Poor, dumb fish. Their very silence condemns them; if only they could give voice to their agonies there would be fewer fishermen!

I had just settled the ward patients for the night and had prepared the leeches in a shallow receiver when the 'phone rang in sister's office. Even then, leeches were somewhat antediluvian, but they were useful for the local abstraction of blood and were much favoured by our old eye surgeon for the relief of congestion. It was quite customary for his patients to be sporting three in a row above the eyebrow. After about an hour, having each taken about three teaspoonfuls of blood, they would drop off, sleepy and happily replete. They were more trouble to put on, being somewhat temperamental; trust sister to leave the job foɪ me! Any perfume or disinfectant was guaranteed to put them off so that the prospective client must be cleansed with plain water and the area to be used left moist and then covered with white lint in which holes had been cut to allow the leech to bite.

Leeches do not like being handled either, so it was necessary to almost fill a test tube with cotton wool, slip in the leech, broad end downwards and then tilt the tube so that the suckers made contact with the skin. Even then, sometimes they were reticent and needed coaxing by smearing the patients' skin with a little sweetened milk, but once they had the right idea they hung on like grim death. As they produced a substance which prevented the clotting of blood, the bleeding often continued after they had fallen off satiated and sometimes it was necessary to apply a stytic to the triangular " bite " mark which was left. Some hospitals used their leeches only once and then destroyed them, but we dropped ours into a jar of strong salt solution after use so that they obligingly vomited and could be used again. " Dracula " in particular was a lusty leech, lighter in pigmentation than his companions and very active. Sister was quite fond of " Dracula."

When the 'phone rang so unopportunely, I put the leeches down on sister's desk while I answered it. " Dracula " was impatient for his feed and made several attempts to escape, so that I had to keep pushing him back with my finger. Then, to delay me further, Pong appeared, but I had good news for him. A patient who had been discharged that afternoon kept a local winkles and whelks stall with jellied eels to boot, and he had left Pong a large brown paper bag of his wares, shelled and ready for consumption. Pong was delighted with his windfall and hurried into the kitchen in search of vinegar. The bag had been waiting on the desk for a considerable time and had become rather moist, so that when he picked it up the bottom fell out, scattering the contents all over the desk, but he was by no means fussy and went back to the kitchen for a basin and swept them all in.

Then, established in sister's chair and with his feet on her desk, he settled down to enjoy his treat, and even the arrival of night sister did not disturb him. She viewed him with disfavour, really! The way that young man bolted his food! A potential gastric ulcer if ever she saw one! She read the report and then, looking round for something to complain of, saw the receiver. " Sister's desk," she said severely, " is no place for that sort of thing! " Actually, she was looking at Pong's boots, but I picked up the receiver to mollify her.

" Dracula! " He was gone! He must have escaped during the cufuffle; no sign of him on the desk either. I gazed in horrid fascination at Pong as he put down his empty basin and smacked his chops in appreciation, then he belched deeply with great satisfaction and began picking his teeth with the trocar which he kept in his pocket for that purpose. Night sister could stand it no longer. " Disgusting man! " she snorted, and swept out like a brig in full sail.

" Virgo intacta! " muttered Pong in retaliation as he ambled out after her. I searched every place but I never did find " Dracula " and his disappearance was one more thing for ward sister to hold against me.

I still continued to feed Daddy Clay his bowl of gruel nocte, and on catching sight of me he would begin to mouth in anticipation. I hoped ward sister would not find out, but before long she was complaining that I used more than my quota of milk. After that, I began getting tins of baby food and sneaking them in under the scarlet cape with which all night nurses were provided. One night, for the first time, he rejected it. He had given up his rowing too, and kept heaving his long, bony legs over the bed boards in an effort to escape. Towards dawn, there was an obvious deterioration in his condition. I tried to remember when it was high water, for they invariably went out with the tide. If he died before eight o'clock I would have to lay him out, but if he lasted until then it would be the day staff's job. Towards eight when I went into feel his pulse he gripped my hand, but his hoary eyes stared right through me and saw me not at all. Feebly, he tried a last " halloo," but in the middle of it his mouth fell slackly to one side and he was gone. Staff nurse, who had just come on duty, stood in the doorway, looking closely at her watch. " He's all yours," she said, and hurried away so that she would be the first to tell sister.

60

We were not allowed to perform " last offices " until at least one hour after death. " A mark of respect," they said, but it also gave time for processes of elimination to be completed; so I would have to come back after " supper " (night staff meals were all back to front!). When she read the report, ward sister was almost cheerful. One day she would smile by mistake and never forgive herself!

When I returned, Stinker's face had settled into that benign expression which so often follows death, and he looked surprisingly young and quite handsome. After I had finished I was very pleased with the result; unloved and unlamented, he lay with the dignity of a patriarch.

The following evening, the ward seemed strangely subdued. As usual, one of the men had saved the local evening paper for me and it lay spread out on the kitchen table. From the front page a familiar face stared up at me, a youthful Clay, bold and stalwart in sou'wester and life jacket.

" Tribute to our Sailor Son! " screamed the headlines.

" Lifeboat coxswain for forty years! "

They had dug deep into their archives; his seamanship was phenomenal, his exploits legion. Countless lives had been saved by his incredible courage and strength, and his refusal to admit defeat. A civic funeral was to be arranged for the hero.

I had many lessons yet to learn, but " Old Stinker " had taught me the most important one of all.

At last I came off night duty, bewitched, bothered and bewildered and a confirmed insomniac. The world had suddenly stopped and was now going the wrong way round. I had four days off, or was it nights? in which to get rehabilitated, and spent them with my sister who was now married and living in Bournemouth.

When I returned to hospital I was back with my own age group. " Torti " Collis, " Pansy " Plant, " Moke " and " Gentle Jane," who had certainly never been christened Jane, and who had tried so hard to buffer me from the hard knocks when I first came. We had all attained status during the past year and I had now been allocated to Out-patients department.

My first morning there was a revelation concerning the things people did to themselves and to one another! And the places they got things stuck in, and the things they got stuck in the places! No wonder sister was a spinster, it was enough to put anybody off. But she was very jolly and a joy to work with. It was her half day, but as she said there was nothing much doing in the afternoon, only the psychiatric clinic and that was nothing — only you had to stand no nonsense from the patients and have all the files ready and in order for Dr. Hatter, the psychiatrist, who was very particular about having all the files ready and the patients lined up correctly. Any fool could do that.

The patients began to arrive far too early; obviously they enjoyed their psychiatric sessions with Dr. Hatter. I took their particulars and sat them down on the benches in the right order, but they would keep jumping up and changing their seats and behaving like unruly children. One was a real upstart and just would not be said. He was a little cartoon-like character with a too long coat, a bowler hat and thick pebble glasses. He would keep bobbing up and down. I got quite cross and took him by the hand and led him to the end of the back bench. He could jolly well wait till last. " Sit there," I said, giving him a little push and he sat. " Now, what name did you say it was? "

" Hatter," he said.

Whenever possible, we participated in the local sport displays. Matron was all for good healthy sport. I was, too; I reckoned to provide for my Christmas and birthday gifts with the proceeds. I once gave a fine ten-day clock as a wedding present, the recipients being dazzled by its munificence until they took it from the box to reveal a card: " 1st Prize. 200 yds."

Most of the sports were held at Canterbury, where the nurses had a sports ground and a huge new white hospital of which they were inordinately proud. There was much rivalry between us. In our own humble way, we also had a sports club which we supported ourselves by self-appointed duties. Pansy, pleated uniform caps at a ha'penny each, Moke polished shoes, I plucked eyebrows — a penny each — and wrote rude rhymes to order. We even dug and delved a small allotment, granted by the grace and favour of matron, and sold the produce to cook. The soil was very mediocre and once, in the dark hours of the night, we crept out in our oldest clobber and robbed a neighbouring farmer of his manure heap. He was furious when he discovered the loss, but never thought to seek it at the hospital next door.

Eventually, our hard earned pennies so increased the club funds, we were able to afford a tennis court. It was a proud achievement and we urgently wrote home for the old rackets which we had wielded at school.

Finding the time to play was another matter, for lectures were all held in our off-duty time, and then they had to be written up in exercise books to be used for swotting at some later date. Even so, the courts were usually occupied on fine evenings after supper, and patients in the wards which overlooked them leaned out of the windows shouting encouragement and advice until night sister doing her rounds shushed them all back to bed.

Hospital exams were of paramount importance, for until they were satisfactorily passed, one was not allowed to enter for the all-important state examinations. At last, after two years of endless chores and interminable lectures and with our hospital exams behind us, we were qualified to take our preliminary state examination. It was a momentous occasion, but costly. Since our training was at a voluntary hospital, we had to fork out the two pounds entrance fee ourselves. Our salaries were fifteen pounds the first year, twenty pounds the second year and twenty-five the third year, but from that was deducted insurance money and money for uniform and study books. Ward sisters, superior beings, actually earned fifty pounds per annum!

In addition to the entrance fee, there was our fare to London where the ordeal was to take place at St. Stephen's Hospital. As usual, father turned up trumps, but we had to have a whip round for Moke.

We each had a chart listing the accomplishments with which we should be familiar and each attainment had to be initialled by a sister verifying our proficiency. Sisters were very chary, however, of signing these documents lest we should, at some later date, prove inefficient and it should be traced back to them. In any case, they always insisted on seeing the chore performed again before their very eyes, and were cross with us for asking because they really hadn't got the time.

Consequently, none of us had our charts up to date, but the railway carriage in which we travelled was very crowded so we passed them round and got them initialled that way. It looked quite authentic and everyone was delighted to oblige.

Our fellow travellers were a jolly lot; they even took part

in our last desperate swotting session, joining happily in the jingles we employed to refresh our memories.

First the symptoms of syphilis:

" There was a young man of Bombay,
Who thought chancres would soon fade away,
Until he got tabes
And gummatas babies
And thought he was Queen of the May."

We were a bit weak, too, on the bones of the wrist, but Tortie, who had recently fractured hers, was well up on this:

Scaphoid.
Semilunar.
Cuneiform.
Pisiform.
Trapezium.
Trapezoid.
Os Magnum.
Unciform.

" Slowly Sailing Cooking Peas Travelling Towards My Ulna," we chanted, and when we reached the great metropolis our fellow passengers went off to their humdrum office jobs muttering, " Slowly Sailing Cooking Peas . . . "

It took us some time to track down St. Stephen's Hospital, but once there we found large arrows directing entrants to the examination room. Our high spirits were sadly depleted now; most of all, we dreaded the compulsory question and when the papers were handed round we covertly rolled our eyes at each other. The enforced question was: " Give the life history of a bug."

Heading our primary paper was a space in which to record any disability from which we might be suffering and which might detract from our performance.

Moke was just recovering from hepatitis, and Tortie still had her wrist in plaster. It was her left, but sister tutor had told her she might mention it for consideration. I felt peeved that they should both have such unfair advantages over me, and just before the papers were collected, I scribbled in my vacant space, " Born in an air raid."

The practical part of the examination took place in the afternoon after a lunch of dubious mince and rice pudding. We stood for hours in a long dark corridor at the top of the building and a lift went constantly up and down creating an infernal draught.

We were blue with cold, when a woman like a teradactyl stuck her head out from a nearby doorway and called, " Nurse Collis! " Torti, with a grimace, followed her in.

We were to go in alphabetical order and poor Pansy, by the time they got to her, was cyanosed and dithering with the cold. The first task alloted to her was to fill an ice bag, and she had to start from scratch with a small pick and a large lump of ice.

When my turn came I was ushered into a room in which tables were heaped with all sorts of hospital equipment, obviously my predecessors had all had a good rummage through it. At another table sat the examiners, and genuine hospital patients sat or lay in beds, waiting to be performed on and looking as though they were having a whale of a time.

The first job I got was to apply a mustard plaster, so I gazed at the jumble on the tables and wondered where to start. One of the examiners who looked vaguely familiar leaned forward. " You'd better get this right," he said. " I think I signed for it." I stared unbelievingly at him, and softly he began to chant, " Slowly sailing cooking peas — "

In spite of everything we passed, and proudly wore white chevrons on our sleeves to substantiate the fact. Now we were really on the way up. Matron gave me the job of senior nurse on the womens' surgical ward and elated, I scrutinised my features in the mildewed mirror of my bedroom. Perhaps I was going to be a swan after all!

There had always been " Trouble in the Balkans," but suddenly the Balkans were a lot nearer; refugees were coming over in droves, camps were set up for them and some, for reasons of health, were admitted to hospital. In their halting speech, they told terrible tales of torture and pleaded piteously for money to bring over their aged Yiddisha mommas, refusing to believe that we had none or that our parents would not be forthcoming if approached. On the back of the office door, Pong pinned a picture. It depicted a small mongrel dog gazing ecstatically at a large poster which bore the legend: " 10,000 Poles for Britain."

Matron gave hospital room to some refugee nurses and

we tried to help them and to improve their limited knowledge of our language, but their methods of nursing were so alien, and they were very critical of ours. To our amazement they insisted on taking to their beds during menstruation (fancy even letting anyone know!) They said it was customary in their native land, but we did not believe it and thought that Hitler was well shut of them.

We had a new student coming and were forewarned that she was very juvenile, just seventeen and straight from school. Matron was taking her to oblige her father, but she would not officially begin her training until she was eighteen, the stipulated age. When she arrived, she was loose-limbed and coltish, with huge brown eyes fringed with black ' sweep's brush ' lashes. They were her only claim to beauty, but when she had learned how to use them she would need nothing else. She was so young it broke your heart, and it was a crying shame to turn her loose amongst us.

Naively, she accounted for herself; she had spent most of her remembered life in kindergartens and boarding schools, but she had a father who was a very dashing lieutenant-commander in the Royal Navy. When he was on leave they had a proper ' beano.' Somewhere, there was a twin sister and a mother, but her parents had been divorced and her mother had custody of her twin and her father of herself. What a carry on we thought, but the dashing father sounded interesting. We inquired when the next beano was due, but he had only recently rejoined his ship. Just our luck!

That first night after ' lights out ' she came scuttling into my room afraid of the dark. I was incredulous and reprimanded her sternly; if she told that to anyone else she was for it. I had once admitted to a fear of spiders and ever since my bed had been a dumping ground for them. She was accustomed to sleeping in dormitories where a dimmed light was kept for convenience, so I saw her back to her own room and left her the torch with which I had been reading under the bedclothes. After that I had a feeling that she spent all her pin money on batteries. She seemed to imagine in me the mother for whom she had been searching for, and I just could not get her off my back. In vain, I told her it was not done for seniors to fraternise with juniors. She dubbed me a " stuffy old fuddy duddy," and was not a whit abashed. Everywhere she dropped clangers, and we were very careful what we gave her to do. Delegated to help the vicar with his communions, she knocked over his improvised alter and came out with a four letter word which was never let loose outside the common room (not the one you're thinking of either, but far, far worse!) Of course, she did not know the meaning, but the dear man was so shocked that he obviously did; which only goes to show that parsons are not so pure as they appear to be.

When instructed to clean the loo with soda water our young student was found squirting our one precious syphon down the S-bend, and when told to deliver a patient in her wheel-chair to the X-ray department, she managed to squeeze the patient, the wheel-chair and herself into the food lift, so that they all ended up in the basement kitchen. Cook, who was expecting the joint, dissolved into hysteria and it took the combined efforts of all the kitchen staff half an hour to release them from the lift, only to find that there was no other way out of the kitchen which had not been built to accommodate wheel chairs. The patient, now inclined to hysteria as well, refused to be sent up alone, so it took them all just as long to pack the intruders back into the lift in order to be rid of them. Dinner was very late that day.

The 'babe,' as she was now known, was so anxious to learn and to redeem herself, that I taught her how to test the urines. Dejectedly, she registered " N.A.D." (nothing abnormal discovered), and longed to find something really exciting. One evening, when we were all rushed off our feet but had nothing we dared give her to do, she decided she would test the urine of all the staff; after all, you never knew what you might find there! Poor Babe, I was afraid she would be disappointed. We all obliged her with a specimen, but I surreptitiously added to mine, a large tablespoonful of glucose. After that we were so hectic, I thought no more of it.

When we came from supper and made our way to our own quarters, Pong was waiting at the stairway. " A word in your ear, wench," he murmured, taking me by the elbow and manoeuvring me into his own doorway. He indicated a chair and by his solemn demeanour I knew that there was something much amiss. My heart missed a beat, it must be something very terrible that I had done. " I'm afraid," he said without preamble, " that it's possible you may be a diabetic."

I had completely forgotten the urine testing, but relief flooded over me deliciously. I had not killed anybody after all! I felt a right gawby, however, when he went on to explain how a tearful Babe had taken my specimen to him and begged him to save me, and it was even worse having to account to her. She quite forgot her previous concern for me and thought only of how I had fooled her. " I'll never forgive you! Never! " she wept, and the juniors stood aghast to hear a senior so addressed.

She soon forgot not to forgive me and was busy vilifying Pong, who persisted in calling her " sweet pea." Despite ourselves, she brought a youthful optimism to our ranks. She also brought the mumps, and one by one the staff succumbed. Practically no one had had it and those who had, only on the one side. Now they had it on the other.

I was due for annual leave but of course it was postponed. I had never caught mumps myself; my early escapade with the night soil appeared to have immunised me against everything. It was very disheartening. Soon, I was the most junior nurse left. In spite of my chevrons, I " ran " between wards doing bedpans and the most menial tasks while sister and staff nurses held the fort in other directions; even matron and the ass. mat. pithered around soothing the fevered brows and getting under everybody's feet.

Then it was Sunday, my twenty-first birthday. No post, no greetings; just one long bed-pan round. From sick bay came the sound of Torti's record player and much merriment; the sufferers were making the most of their convalescence. Oh well, one good thing to come out of it; at twenty-one I was old enough to take my State Final.

Finally, things were back to normal except for the refugees who continued to pour into the country. Resentment grew against them for there were so many, and soon they would be taking us over and probably half of them were spies anyway. The ass. mat. in particular disliked Jews. Supervising meals at the head of the table, she persisted in making offensive remarks when the Jewish nurses were present, and this we found intolerable. Once, as senior present and seated at her right hand to assist her with the serving, I could bear it no longer. After a particular snyde comment from her, I rose with what I hoped was dignity: " Sister," I said, " you are obviously unaware that my father is a chief Rabbi," and as I stalked out, hoping that Rabbis were not celibate, I heard her say: " I always thought what a big nose she'd got! "

It had taken courage because I knew that consequently I had lost my supper, but when the others came up Babe was secreting a crust and a large lump of cheese under her apron.

" You were wonderful! " she cried. " Why ever didn't you tell us before about your father? Gosh! A Rabbi! That's the most exciting thing ever — next to a lieutenant-commander."

Babe was now beginning to prove her worth, having shown that at least she could detect sugar she was given urine testing to do. She always excelled at ' doing ' the flowers, a chore we found very time consuming and tedious, though we had to impress on her that she must never mix red and white blooms together in the same vase, otherwise dire consequences would result.

Meanwhile, a new wonder drug had come into use. It was given by intra-muscular injection and was known as " Prontosil." Because of it, a desperate case of meningitis who would normally have died, recovered completely, and several miracle cures followed. We rejoiced accordingly, and decided the whole field of medicine would be revolutionised.

Our sports club provided for an annual trip to London to see a show, in two separate groups of course; one marshalled by matron and the other by the ass. mat. It was a highlight of the year and we held many meetings in the common room to decide the all important choice as to which show it should be. This year had been whittled down to Victoria Regina or The Balalika, and when finally it was put to the vote The Balalika won by two. " Oh! " wailed the Babe from the back row, " and I did so want to see Victoria's Vagina."

Soon, it was another highlight; carnival time again, and this year, to represent the hospital, matron had chosen outpatient's sister (beloved by all the townsfolk), and an astute staff nurse of Scotch origin who would be responsible for the finance which, after all, was the aim of the project, Pong, the Babe and myself, with one of the hall porters to keep us all in order. Babe was beside herself with delight and I was not a little chuffed myself. We transformed our vehicle into a mock operating theatre, the patient being evilly constructed from pillows and artificial limbs. As we swayed through the streets, the two

69

men, decked out in surgeon's garb, endlessly withdrew coils of rubber tubing from its abdomen, to the ghoulish joy of the crowds.

We were voted "best in show," and our collection broke all records. Holiday makers, a kaleidoscope of colour, danced round us in happy abandonment as though to blind themselves to the future. It was a day of sunshine lived to the full.

"The best day of my life," enthused Babe, but we beamed on her indulgently for she was always having "best days." Now, viewing the festive picture of us all, snapped by a beach photographer, it is hard to believe that in a matter of days we were at war.

4.

I was working in the theatre when I heard war declared, the operating surgeon having brought in a portable wireless, thereby creating a precedent. The patient, a Czech refugee, was for Caesarean section, and the child was being delivered through her abdominal wall as the fatal words were spoken. Almost immediately, the sirens began to wail. We all eyed each other and wondered where we had left our gas-masks. It was generally believed that gas warfare would predominate and everyone had been warned to be always prepared, but very soon the all-clear came over. It had only been an unidentified plane bringing, it was rumoured, the Duke of Windsor.

For a time, everything remained quiet and it was all a bit of an anti-climax. But not for long. Insidiously, a magnetic mine belt had been laid around our bit of coast, and efficiently, with ceaseless repetition, ships were blown out of the water. Usually, there was a distant boom rattling all the windows and sending us scurrying to prepare beds and fix up drip salines for the survivors. Sometimes, there were no survivors at all; and after the golden summer, winter had come early with a biting cold, and many of the shipwrecked perished before the lifeboats could reach them.

I was put in charge of the childrens' ward, though answerable to sister on the nearby womens' ward. It had been cleared of children, except for the side wards, and had been filled to capacity with government beds: horrid contraptions that folded up the middle, usually when you least wanted them to.

One of the first ships to be wrecked was the Mastiff, ironically a minesweeper. The four survivors were in the sea for five hours before being picked up, and the sea was frozen for the first time in living memory.

"What have we got this time?" I asked the junior who was escorting them up from casualty.

"Three whites and a lascar," she replied, and the lascar sat up spluttering to reveal himself to be the chief engineer covered in oil. Of the others, one was so severely burned, and so extensively that newspapers had already reported him dead; another had the most appalling head injuries, yet was incredibly conscious and lucid, and had been pleading with the lifeboatmen to be thrown back into the sea. The last had a battered face and two fractures of the skull, but he looked as though he might make it. The first head injury case we mercifully kept under morphine until he died. Later, two women, wan after an interminable journey, arrived to see him. I had to go down to the mortuary to renew his dressings before I dared take them. They were his mother and fiancé, and they were past tears.

For one terrible fortnight, not a day or night passed without at least one ship falling foul of the mines. Government beds extended to the coridors and every available space, and a full night's sleep was something which had only happened in the dim past. Townsfolk, too, with one accord turned out to help with rescue work; all suitable vehicles helped supplement ambulance services and sea-worthy boats helped the overworked lifeboats.

One night, roused by night sister, we trundled wearily downstairs to find the large entrance hall choc-a-block with hysterical Lascars, over forty in all. They had just been rescued from the sea and were slimy with oil, and not one spoke any English. Simultaneously, the town's electricity supply was cut. Hours passed before it was restored and the ensuing chaos was indescribable, as with foraged torches, we sorted the living from the dead, the badly injured from the not so bad, the not so bad from the uninjured. The latter were the ones making the most noise and they were taken in by local hoteliers.

The most badly injured were with us for a very long time; there was Ali-Ram-Jam and Ali-Ram-Hasi (they were all Ali's) and they would happily have stayed with us for ever. The other patients taught them a jargon of English and they had only to see anyone in a white coat or even slightly resembling a doctor, to sit up in bed rubbing their bellies and wailing " Plenty much pain backside! "

Slowly, the Navy got the uppermost of the mine belt and wrecks became less frequent, but instead the town was echoing with the tramp of boots and the trundle of heavy vehicles as the army paused briefly en route for Dover and embarkation. During their respite a virulent attack of food poisoning decimated their ranks (many hinted at germ warfare), and our government beds were commandeered for soldiers. The senior service was very resentful: it was their billet and they warned us to have no truck with the army, and the army, knowing what sailors are, cautioned us against them.

One night, going off duty, I called for Pansy on the way, and found her in despair. " I've got a right lot in now," she cried. " They're supposed to be British but they can't speak a word of English." Perhaps they were fifth columnists, I thought, and curious to see these phenomena, I followed her into the ward where a motley crew sat up in their beds. One still had his cap on. They all stared at me and the hatted one called out: " Yoh 'ave a goo at thissun, Bill, 'er doh luk sa sawney as t'other beesum. Goo on yer, blether yed. Aks 'er afore yoh bost! "

" Bill " looked at me miserably, but without much hope. " Wheer's the double yew, nus? " he pleaded, " I wanta cack."

Grudgingly, ward sister allowed me to visit the Black Country crew during my free time to get them sorted out, but she was very hostile, for they tried her sorely. She considered I was of the same ilk, and once more, in her illogical way, attributed them to me. Poor sister! The government beds alone had a traumatic effect upon her tidy mind. They were elongated and angular and amongst the hospital beds, stuck out like sore fingers. Worse still, instead of two neat rows like soldiers on parade, she had to have a row down the middle of her ward as well; it was always getting pushed out of line, and her lovely aspidistra, which had taken pride of place for so long, had been banished to the sluice. It had been the unenviable lot of the junior probationer to tend the monster and polish its massive leaves daily with olive oil, but now, abused and out of sight, it became the butt for everyone's spite when they fell foul of sister's spleen.

I was always sure of a warm welcome from my " compatriots " and we enjoyed a good dialectal arjey-barjey, to the mystification of the other members of the ward. They were soon up and about again and one day I was surprised to find them all missing except Sandy Banks. Sandy sought to explain their absence with decorum: " It's ockard like," he bawked, scratching his close cropped ginger poll (sister had confiscated his cap). " They aye 'ere 'cos they air bin, but they'n 'ad summat wot'll mek 'em goo an' when they'n bin they'll cum."

Later, when we took chairs and clustered round the coal fire at the end of the ward, where it was cosier, they cried out in alarm as sister, collecting clients for the padre, paused pen in hand demanding: " Any of you want communion in the morning? "

" Yo' mus' be coddin'! " bellucked " Slasher " Perry. " We doh waent nought! Strewth! We'en bin sot on miskin 'til we nigh on tuk root. We' em that clemmed we ballys think we throat's cut."

" What exactly did he say? " Sister inquired of me coldly.

" He said, ' No thank you,' sister," I replied, and she stalked off unbelieving and in high dudgeon.

" Why the franzy ines! " chuntered " Charlie " Peace, " 'er doh atta cum 'ere wee 'er arse in 'er 'ond. I wouldn't 'arf like ter put a backerapper up 'er appund! "

In the quieter moments we reminisced nostalgically of Clent Hills and Kinver Edge, and mourned sadly for the lost beauty of Baggeridge Woods, which they told me was condemned to the axe. But soon they were gone, swept up into the evil machinations of war.

Pong, too, had deserted us to become a ship's doctor. The new house surgeon was brilliant at surgery and the art of seduction, and to aid his philandering he had a little Tin Lizzie. Her doors were tied together with pieces of string and anyone tempted aboard with amorous intent usually had their ardour cooled by having to help push her back. We were amused by his Casanovian capers, and dubbed him " Cas " for convenience.

Ships continued to go down, but less frequently; the latest was a French vessel and her crew, not too badly injured, were cheekily charming and wholly delightful. Enchanted by our schoolroom French, they had no difficulty in making themselves understood.

" Darling je vous aime beaucoup,
Je ne sais pas what to do."

To our joy, the ass. mat., always so boastful of her accomplishments, was revealed to have no French at all, and after the first encounter made herself scarce. The Mastiff's burned stoker and fractured gun-layer, banished to a side ward, scowled and glowered, making rude remarks about " froggies " and developing unspecified symptoms to draw attention to themselves.

Cas was beside himself with fury and resorted to a French unknown in any schoolroom, parried by slick repartees from the Frenchies. It was a gay interlude.

The stoker and the gun-layer were our oldest inhabitants, and took on proprietary rights. Now ambulant, they had become efficient and adaptable in relieving us of fundamental chores and sought to make themselves indispensable. They would have been transferred to a Naval Hospital long since had not those establishments been full to overflowing. Cas was most anxious to be rid of them and schemed to hoof them out, but we fooled him by keeping bandages on their injuries for longer than was necessary. Matron turned a blind eye to our subterfuge; she disapproved strongly of Cas and obstructed his every move on principle. Also, the Royal Navy coughed up two pounds for daily maintenance, which was corn in Egypt!

Christmas was in sight, and rehearsals for our traditional concert were in full swing when it was decided that the State Final examination, postponed at the outbreak of war, should now take place at Canterbury instead of London. Lectures and studies had been at a standstill for so long, the ass. mat., whose duties extended to that of sister tutor, doubted we would make it except perhaps the knowledgeable Torti — Pansy, Moke and myself had always been laggards. We thought bitterly of the days when you could buy your S.R.N. and speculated on how many of our superiors might have come by it that way. The ass. mat. kept hinting that, with the Finals looming imminent, I should forgo my part in the concert this year. I would sooner have given up the finals. Besides, I had composed a rhyme incorporating all the senior staff, ridiculing their own peculiar foibles. It was rather impertinent, but wedded to a popular tune and performed by Babe, who could get away with anything, it would be a riot. Babe was delighted with her performance and wondered if perhaps she was depriving the world of a great artiste by taking up with the mundane job of nursing.

Magnanimously, the day before our examination, matron gave us finalists a buckshee day off. The others decided to spend it swotting, but last minute cramming had never done anything for me, and I decided to spend it with my friend, 'Gina. Although severely disabled with arthritis, 'Gina lived alone and her incapacities were compensated by a dry wit and a nimble mind. On fine days, with my help, she would make it to the shore where she loved to be, and we would watch fascinated as 'planes, equipped at the base with a huge metal ring, skimmed the sea, and thus attracted to the surface magnetic mines which they promptly machine gunned. Since the weather had deteriorated, however, we had begun to decorate her little flat and this day off was a welcome bonus. Inevitably, it began with a " lie in," for I knew that when the others came up to make their beds after breakfast, someone would bring me a tray of tea and toast and marmalade. It was something we always did for each other.

This time it was the faithful Babe who was wild with excitement as she plonked down my tray with a clatter, and flung herself on to the bed, her arms round my neck. Really, she would never learn to show respect! She had just received a letter from her wonderful, wonderful father, who would be on leave in a few days so that another beano was due. Unable to control herself, she rolled about my bed like a young puppy.

Sternly, I took her to task and reminded her that tomorrow I was taking my State Final. Immediately, her mood changed and she sat up in consternation: " Oh," she wailed, " I haven't got your mascot yet and I'm not off till this evening and the shops 'll be closed! " (It was usual for potential examinees to be given mascots by their friends). Then with mercurial charm, she brightened. " Silly old mascots. I'll do something practical instead. I'll get your uniform ready, sew on the buttons and everything."

Now that was something, for I hated sewing; buttons were always coming adrift and the uniform I was to wear for my exam must be meticulous and above reproach. Delighted to be in favour again she bounced off my bed, and as she hared down the corridor I could hear her carolling her Christmas concert song. And it was supposed to be so hush-hush until the first performance!

76

That day, 'Gina and I papered her living room, and by the time we had finished clearing up it was nearly nine o'clock. I fetched a fish and chip supper from the corner shop and we ate it out of the paper to save washing up, after which it was a mad dash to get back to the hospital before the doors were locked at ten. As I hurried off, 'Gina's good wishes for the morrow reminded me of the forthcoming ordeal.

It was very parky and a chill mist drifted in from the sea; hardly a night to wait for buses. As I went along at a jog trot, gas mask case bumping rhythmically against my rump, the streets were dark and all the windows shuttered. Who was it who said the lights were going out all over Europe? I was nearly home and dry before the darkened bus rumbled by and was glad I had walked. How lucky I was to have a friend like 'Gina and to be always sure of a warm welcome.

I had nearly reached the hospital gates when I passed the dark shape of an army truck pulled up at the roadside, probably some soldier and his girl croodling together. A few yards further on, a darkish patch in the road caused me to pause and shine my torch. I went over to it and found an unconscious female, still alive despite severe head injuries. I tried to think what I must do, remembering that internal injuries were sometimes inflicted by the indiscriminate moving of accident cases, but all I could think was that a bus was due from the opposite direction and that she lay in the path of it. I took off my cloak, spread it out beside her, and gently eased her on to it. A pochette, a small envelope type handbag commonly used at that time lay on the road and I picked it up, since it might have some form of identification. As I dragged her to the kerb, two dark shapes stumbled from the vicinity of the army truck; soldiers, young and frightened in the torchlight. With their dimmed truck lights they had seen nothing, only felt the impact, and now as he realised what had happened, the driver began to vomit. The other soldier helped me to lift her onto the grass verge and as we did so the darkened bus to town trundled past without stopping.

When I pointed out the hospital gates and asked them to tell the hall porter and bring a stretcher, the soldier hurried off, heartened to have something constructive to do. As I sat with the injured girl's head in my lap, the grey mist wreathing us and white frost rimming the grasses, blood seeped stickily through my thin skirt. It was obvious she was dying. Somewhere, people as yet unknown would mourn tonight. I wondered if there was any form of identification; her clothes were sodden with mud and blood and her face was just a pulp, but there was the pochette. It revealed only a screwed up handkerchief with a sixpence knotted in the corner, a bus ticket and a folded newspaper cutting. I smoothed it out and in the waning torchlight, eerily saw a photograph of myself. I knew it well, it had featured in a daily paper, snapped to my great discomfiture when I attended survivors from a shipwreck. I had felt a right Charlie and had suffered much ragging in consequence. What a coincidence! Maybe she had known the man I was attending to. Carefully, I refolded the cutting and put it back. Soon, wavering storm lanterns and the tramp of feet heralded the arrival of the stretcher. I wrapped the girl more closely in my cloak to conceal from the boy soldiers the dreadful injuries, but when we reached the entrance hall the dim blackout lights revealed little except that she was in extremis.

The night staff, already alerted, took over. " You'd better go and get cleaned up," said night sister, viewing me with some distaste. " And take those noisy girls to task." Wild sounds were floating down from the nurses' quarters. It sounded like an Irish wake. In the common room I found a crowd of juniors surrounding one of their contemporaries who appeared to be having hysterics. There was a sudden respectful silence when I walked in until the hysterical one, catching sight of me, gory and dishevelled in the sudden light, set off again with her banshee wailing. Heartily I slapped her down until she sobered up sufficiently to sob out her story.

" It was our evening off and we went to the pictures. When we came back on the bus, Babe ran straight across the road . . . "

The jigsaw of events was falling into a horrific pattern. That bloodstained bundle, the poor battered face, the photograph of myself! What a blind idiot I had been! Slowly, like a zombie, I turned and walked back down the stairs.

At last, when all was said and done and I escaped to my room, there laid out on the bed was Babe's last act of homage, clean uniform, painstakingly patched and every button in situ. I found out later she had cut them off her own uniform to replace the missing ones. When I wore it the next morning, the starched harsh calico lining gave the rough satisfaction of a hair shirt.

78

Silently, we set off for Canterbury, and as we waited at the bus-stop we tried to avert our eyes from the blood stain on the road. It had run down into the gutter to trickle wastefully into the nearest drain and later, despite our efforts with buckets of water and bleaches, it persisted, a mute reminder, until the snows came and covered it.

At Canterbury, we found the great white hospital, once the pride and joy of our rivals, was camouflaged a dirty grey and all its beauty gone. We never could recall what questions were asked of us or what duties we had to perform, but afterwards we turned into the cathedral and sat in silent contemplation. Christmas came and went; no-one would ever sing Babe's song. All staff festivities were cancelled and instead of gifts to each other we contributed to a memorial picture for the little chapel. The war had caught up with us, but Babe was only the first to go.

At the end of January, our exam results came through, proclaiming Pansy, Moke and myself as State Registered Nurses. Torti, the pick of the bunch had failed. She accepted it philosophically, but we were stunned by the injustice of it all. The patients cheered when we self-conciously went on duty in our black petersham belts and with strings and a bow added to our Sister Dora caps. Actually, they were not attached to the caps as everyone imagined, but were just a length of starched tape with a ready-made bow stitched on halfway along. The bow was placed under the chin and the the two ends of tape tied on top of the head, after which the starched white cap was placed on top (and surreptitiously secured with a hat pin). The prim unyielding bow scratched constantly under the chin, as did the harsh tape behind the ears, but the little knot on top of the head was worst of all, for there was constant friction, resulting eventually in a little bald patch where the hair was worn away.

I was by now on night duty again, but this time as " runner," which meant that I was a general factotum helping out wherever needed, visiting each ward in turn to check drugs, assisting in theatre, hand-maiden to night sister and Cas. In short, a general dogs-body. The pace was fierce, but it was great. Cas had heard of the fiasco of my twenty-first, and when my birthday came round again, made it an excuse for celebration. He provided the drinks and the " eats," and night sister gave her blessing. She commanded more respect amongst the staff than anyone, and when she stipulated soft drinks only for the night staff and " no nonsense " for the day staff she knew her word was law. Moreover, she could keep an eye on Cas's intake, which was a welcome change! The patients were given the option of sherry or " Black Jack " when the medicine trolley went round, and at supper next morning night sister produced a bottle of vintage wine for good conduct. I decided it was worth a nose bleed.

One night, when we went down to breakfast, we heard that during the day the Royal Navy had arrived unheralded and carried off Stoker and Gun-layer. We felt quite disconsolate; things wouldn't be the same without them. After a few days, however, they re-appeared, for their base was only at near-by Chatham and they were being given survivor's leave. After so long the hospital felt like home, and it was only natural to come back. Everyone was delighted to see them and even matron unbent a little, though she now had to forfeit her two pounds a day.

When they arrived we had just gone up to our quarters but were called down to see them.

Gun-layer manoeuvred me into a corner. " Let's get married," he said urgently.

" But who'd have us? " I asked.

They stayed around for some time, then Stoker went home to London where he was promptly knocked down by a taxi and wrote to say he was back in hospital with fifteen stitches in his leg. It was one of matron's most rigorous rules that we should not go out with ex-patients, but one morning before going to bed I went with Gun-layer to ' The Smuggler,' famous for home made scones topped with thick cream and home-made jam. Their stocks hadn't yet run out, but it was unfortunate that the ass. mat. should have chosen the same time to go. When I got back she was waiting to usher me into the matron's office. I didn't repeat the error!

The long harsh winter still raged without abatement and bleak winds scoured the coast. No wonder the local herrings were distinguished by their blue gills! February brought the snow, silently, stealthily by night, concealing the camouflaged buildings, the stacked sandbags, the stain on the road, and bringing traffic to a standstill. Few people got through to the hospital, except one of the honorary surgeons in a red pom-pom hat, proud of his prowess on skis, and Gun-layer.

Gun-layer had been assigned to another ship, the *Jarvis Bay*. It was a good berth, he said, and before long he hoped to be a gunner's mate. What a funny thing to want to be! And I had imagined that he wanted to be mine!

Gradually, the roads cleared, but the snow lingered on into March. Food rationing had begun and with it our diet improved. We had never had butter on the menu before!

There was an uneasy quiet in the war situation; beds became vacant and long-awaited hospital waiting lists began to get attention again. Like all hospitals, we had our malingerers, and such a one was " Burper " Belcher, one of our regulars. Sometimes he might call ' wolf ' once too often and damn us forever with a rejected perforated appendix, but when he arrived at two o'clock one morning simulating agony, Cas, unacquainted with him, was inveigled into admitting him for observation. Mr. Belcher liked nothing better than to be " observed." He was most proficient in making his thermometer register incorrectly if attended by the unwary, in regulating his respirations and in swallowing air, so that he became a distended wind bag punctuating the night with eructations.

After submitting happily to a week of intensive investigation which revealed nothing abnormal, the Burper, blissfully somnolent after an injection of distilled water, fell out of bed and Torti, unable to budge him and fearful he might at last have done himself a mischief, summoned help. Cas and I arrived simultaneously to find him prone on the floor and with stertorous breathing. Cas made a cursory examination before taking a jug of iced water from an adjoining locker and pouring it over him. Mr. Belcher sat up spluttering and very aggrieved; " Sorry, old chap," said Cas cheerfully, " Seems there's nothing can be done for your condition." He took down the chart and scrawled across the still vacant space for diagnosis, " Oscillans Plumbi," and later on I saw the Burper surreptitiously copying it onto a scrap of paper. Tomorrow he would go home a happy man, boasting of an affliction for which science knew no cure. I did hope that no Latin linguist would ever enlighten him!

Cas, always something of a tippler, had now begun to make merry with associates in the town. Oftentimes, he would just make it to the driveway, where he would sit rendering to the night air, bawdy rugger songs in his fruity Irish brogue until night sister and I hurried down to winkle him out of the Tin Lizzie and lug him upstairs to his quarters, there to lock him in and pray that we wouldn't have need of him. Not unnaturally, after such bouts he became sullen and belligerent. At one time, he suspected a porter of making free with his liquor and to catch the culprit, doctored a bottle with croton oil (a most drastic purgative which promotes excruciating peristalsis). Then coming home inebriated, he drank it himself! Nemesis indeed! For several nights he traipsed around, two double with pain, filching alleviates from the medicine cupboards and swearing abstinence.

Of course, it did not last. Then came the crunch. Matron was away for a few days when Cas chose to entertain his friends. Sounds of revellry pervaded the first floor and indignant thumpings on his door by the ass. mat. evoked no response until 2 a.m. when it flew open, erupting on to the corridor a conglomeration of young medicos in their underpants. Hairy appendages with door-knocker knees, torsoes like doormats; small wonder male nudes never caught on!

Most were known to us but were quite unrecognisable since they all wore gas masks. Like Cerce's swine, they swarmed downstairs, and from sounds below it was obvious they were doing a round of the wards. Cries of " Brandy! Brandy! Whoopee!" indicated the medicine cupboards were being raided. In no time at all they were back upstairs and trooping along to the male surgical ward, followed by the ass. mat. wringing her hands, and night sister wrathful and incredulous at having her authority flouted

I was working on the female surgical ward, the nurse there being unwell, and there were a number of very ill patients. Drawn out in the corridor by the carousel, I was joined by Nurse Donna, one of the evacuee nurses who was in charge of the childrens' ward next door. We stared at each other aghast, obviously we were next on the list. Bella (she just had to be Bella), breathed heavily down her nose; " Nevair in mine country could such a thing come to pass," she snorted, but this was no time for censure. There were no locks on the double doors leading to the wards, only large " grab " handles on the inside of them, so the thing was to tie the handles securely together. Bandages were not strong enough, so we took off our long black woollen stockings. Bella went inside her ward and wove her stockings through and around the handles, finishing with a tight knot. I pushed hard but the doors stood firm. Hurriedly, I went into my ward and did the same just as the mob arrived. Furious and frustrated, they clamoured and pushed, while from my side I pushed back. Our stockings were tough and durable. The doors parted slighty and as a hand snaked through I bit hard on it and it was withdrawn with a yowl of pain and indignation. Eventually, the rabble went away. They were beginning to sober up and there was quiet except for a whimpering from some of the patients.

Matron was recalled the next morning. There was a board meeting and poor, foolish, talented Cas walked the wards no more.

The inclement weather persisted and the cold was still intense, most opportune, matron decided, for me to take my long overdue holidays. I had originally planned to visit an ex-colleague in Cambridge and decided to still do so. The short time left to me was fraught with preparation. There was 'Gina to visit, my room to turn out and vacate in readiness for my successor, the washing and ironing of my personal things and finally, packing. No time for sleep by day and on duty by night. By the time my holiday began, I was exhausted. Gun-layer, still marking time before sailing, promised to see me at the station. I would still have to travel via London, he said.

Of course, I missed my train, but Gun-layer was still waiting. He had, he explained, got leave. It was marriage leave. (In fact, if he returned unwed there would be the devil to pay!) He was armed with a special licence. That must have cost him a pretty packet. I could never abide waste!

The station was crowded. I was not sure if it was that more people were travelling or just less trains, but I was indescribably weary and had the feeling that the world was going round anti-clockwise. Gun-layer, ever practical, suggested that he should join the long queue at the ticket office while I made inquiries as to the time of departure and platform for the London train. Everyone seemed to be trying to find out the same thing, and there appeared to be no means of finding out. A rather aloof porter stood well away from the milling throng doing absolutely nothing, but when I approached him with my query, he looked down his nose at me and said: " I really don't know, madam."

I was astonished at his unhelpful attitude.

"But you should know," I cried. "It's your job to know." I became more heated when he raised a cynical eyebrow and gave him a few more home truths until I caught sign of Gun-layer from a distance signalling agitatedly.

Petulantly, I walked over to him. "Hey, what are you doing" he said, ' talking to our chief petty officer? "

We were married at Caxton Hall. Gun-layer bought the ring en route and also a hat, which he considered was an essential for me. It was a marina-green pill-box affair. I cannot remember which dress I wore, but I think it was one I had bought off Moke for two bob after she had scorched a large hole in the back. I had always admired the front, and the back didn't show with a coat on. We had quite forgotten the need for witnesses, but a Canadian soldier and his girl, who had just braved the Atlantic to marry him, offered their services. Their names were Hilda and John. We had a meal together afterwards and never saw them again.

London was brave and gay under the blackout, having her last fling before the holocaust. Gun-layer was quite affluent with his accumulation of back pay (and I had all of ten bob!) We saw the latest shows; *Gulliver's Travels, The Wizard of Oz* and the *Crazy Gang* singing " Run Rabbit Run," with the very rabbit (so they assured us), which had been the first air-raid casualty of the war.

I had wired my friend at Cambridge and perfidiously sent her my mail for reposting. Meanwhile, we were staying at a little hotel in Westminster, quite cut off from the world we knew. The proprietors were kindly indulgent, but I was thrown into turmoil when they offered to get the name changed on my ration book. Matron would throw a fit. I am afraid they thought the worst of me.

I returned to day duty, staffing on the medical wing, and wondering what would happen if they found out? Married nurses were quite taboo. Gun-layer was again in limbo, for during our absence, the *Jarvis Bay* had sailed without him, unexpectedly and under secret orders. He mourned inordinately, but she and all his shipmates had gone to a glorious end and comp'ete annihilation. He still haunted the vicinity during his free time but soon he was assigned to another ship and was gone. It was as though he had never been, except for a wedding ring on a bit of string around my neck.

This was to set the pattern of our lives, for during the next six years we were destined to spend less than six months together. Leaves were so often given abroad, in Australia, in Capetown (home of the Captain!), or on some remote tropical island. Letters were infrequent and censored. One night, after duty, I confided in Gentle Jane. We had always been close and I knew she would never tell. One day, Stoker came to see us again. Gun-layer, he warned us, was now a married man, the sly old salt! Oh well, you know what sailors are! Everyone looked pityingly at me. I was glad I had told Jane.

Work on the medical wing was of a slower tempo to that on the surgical wards. The new drug Prontosil continued to work wonders; though while on it patients must never partake of eggs, onions, or any form of salts, otherwise it acted as a poison. Unhappily, when our stocks were exhausted, there was no more forthcoming, for it was a Bayer product and of German origin and ' Bella ' Donna went around looking more smug than ever.

But new drugs were being produced to replace it. We had always been taught that pneumonia patients lived or died according to the nursing and so we took great pride in seeing that they lived. Now, however, they were treated with M&B 125 which produced extreme nausea. We tried giving it in milk, honey and other recommendations, but despite our efforts, they continued to vomit, succumbing from exhaustion and dehydration. Bitterly, we opposed the new treatment and reverted to known procedures. Much later, in time for Mr. Churchill's pneumonia, came M&B 693 and success.

Meanwhile, air raids were becoming more vicious; the town suffered severe bombing and an enemy plane, attempting to dive-bomb the hospital, crashed. We admitted the pilot and he was given every care until the authorities were able to collect him. We were near to a large aerodrome and there was talk of evacuating the civilian population. Reluctantly, 'Gina went to her sister in Derbyshire and the following week her little flat was demolished by one of our own shells. So much for our decorating.

I had kept in touch with my old hospital via my friend, Wally-bags, who was now staffing there. Wally could never be persuaded to write letters and I always enclosed the reply to my epistle, giving alternatives to my queries so that she had only to delete what was irrelevant and post it. Now, I had a letter from my former matron offering me the position of relief sister there. When I showed it to matron, she advised me to take it, at least temporarily, for it was obvious that many of us would have to go elsewhere during the uncertain conditions and so I accepted it.

The old clique was breaking up and we went our various ways. Pansy Plant was off to London where she had an excellent post and a date with a doodle-bug; Torti Collis must find another training school from which to resit her state final, and Moke, bewitched by the posters, succumbed to nursing the Senior Service and was soon drafted abroad to die miserably of an obscure fever. Jane, an only child, must take a job which would also enable her to care for her semi-invalid widowed mother, and across the years and the miles she is still doing just that.

I found my old stamping ground surprisingly the same. It was I who had changed. The old folk at home were delighted to have me near again; their welcomeness embraced me, but I was consumed with guilt, for I still could not bring myself to confess of my espousement and the wedding ring hung like a millstone round my neck.

When I had relieved each of the ward sisters in turn for their annual leave, I took on night sister's duties, for " Calamity " had retired and had not been replaced. The area was as yet unbreached by bombs, but pestered with alerts when enemy planes passed over en route for richer targets. The urgency of the alerts was indicated by a code of colours given via the 'phone, and when it reached red, all the staff were roused and the patients, on their heavy iron frames or in cumbersome plaster cases, were placed under their beds from where they all immediately demanded bed pans! Meanwhile, down in the village, the vicar ran about like one demented, ringing a hand bell and calling his flock to shelter.

It was decided to equip each of us with a pass which would enable us to return unhindered if we were caught out during raids. These were like glorified passports bearing a photograph together with our credentials, and we had to present ourselves with them in matron's office in order that she might add her signature to verify their authenticity.

86

As she was about to sign mine, I felt impelled to stay her. "It's incorrect," I said lamely and she waited unpeturbed, pen still poised, for an explanation. When I had given it she was, as ever, practical and uncondemning. She offered to get my name on everything documental, but stipulating that in return I must tell my parents without further delay. I had no option now, and they accepted the confession as being typical of my wilfulness and hid their hurt, so that I was more conscience-smitten than ever. At matron's suggestion, I began to "bank" my off-duty against such time as my husband should get leave, and as the months passed, it totted up encouragingly.

We all listened to the traitorous voice of Lord Haw Haw, and waxed hilarious at his menacing implications, but sometimes he was more informative than the nine o'clock news. One night he alluded threateningly to Gun-layer's ship, "Germany calling! Germany calling! We are after you *Sussex*, we know your whereabouts." It was more than I did!

"Jaysus!" ejaculated Wally-bags, crossing herself piously, "Bad cess to the blackguards and bring the boyo home!"

Her prayer was answered, for a few days later I had a 'phone call from Gun-layer himself and he was home! His ship had docked at Liverpool for supplies and the crew had high hopes of leave, for it was obvious they were due for a long spell at sea, but when none was forthcoming and they were about to sail again, someone (it was never discovered who) threw a spanner in the turbines rendering the great ship helpless and at the mercy of the raiders who had tracked her down. The crew were dispersed until she could be repaired and their unknown benefactor was the toast of them all. Gun-layer, unsure of where I might be, had sent a telegram which father had apprehensively opened, and then met him at the station. The parents, said my husband, were being very hospitable. Mother said she had known they would have a visitor for she had dropped a knife on the floor and also there had been a 'stranger on the bars' of the old coal fireplace.

I claimed my accumulated leave and was given permission to go home, but as I sat in the train, a terrible thought struck me. My husband would be waiting for me at the station, but what if I did not recognise him? It had been an awful long time. I tried to visualise him and could not. A currently popular song, *The Sailor With The Navy Blue Eyes* pursued me.

What colour were his? I hauled my baggage off the rack and under cover of the lid rummaged for his photograph. Anxiously, I scrutinised it and was immediately reassured. Of course! He would still have the large indented scar on his forehead.

Would he recognise me? Perhaps I should have told him I would wear a red carnation or something. But when I stepped down onto the old familiar platform, there was no confusion. He was in uniform.

They were halycon days and it was summertime; we climbed Clent Hills, lay on the high sunbaked plateau of Kinver Edge and picnicked on Penn common, but I was anguished by the mutilated stumps of Baggeridge woods. People ran to touch Gun-layer's broad sailor collar " for luck," and we remembered with gratitude our unknown benefactor, the spanner thrower. Gun-layer had brought me twenty-four pairs of sheer silk stockings from America and I purred with luxuriance; they flattered the new short skirts too, for we had been cautioned to economise on materials and had patriotically raised our hems to help the war effort.

We made a brief pilgrimage to London, sunbathing by the Serpentine, in Green Park and in Kensington Gardens; only the almost imperceptible hum of distant traffic betrayed the great metropolis around us. Of course, we stayed at the little hideout in Westminster, thereby establishing our respectability, which seemed important to Gun-layer. The small hotel enfolded us in its warm embrace for the last time. We would come again, we said. But when we finally did so, we found only a hole in the ground.

Travelling back, the train was crowded with child evacuees, all hung about with little treasures and labelled like small parcels for alien destinations. After the first few tearful miles, their natural resilience took over and they chatted intrepidly of the adventures ahead. Those in our compartment carried buckets and spades as part of their equipment for they were, they said excitedly, being sent to the seaside. Laconically, their labels proclaimed " DUDLEY PORT."

Gun-layer, whose parents had divorced when he was a child, was a Yorkshireman. Next time, he said, we would explore the Dales, the Butter-tubs, the old Roman encampments and the Cock-Beck, which had run red with blood during the Wars of the Roses, and we would walk together on Ilkley moor " ba' tat."

Finally, came the last evening, the last possible train. Father was fire watching and mother had diplomatically gone to visit one of her cronies. One thing my husband never had was mother-in-law problems. Reluctantly, we set off for the station.

" Wish me luck as you wave me goodbye," pleaded a near by radio.

" Is your journey really necessary? " demanded the railway posters.

We waited on the same platform from which for years I had embarked unwillingly to school in Wolverhampton, thinking myself a well seasoned traveller. Wolverhampton! Gun-layer had sailed the world over, had taken part in running the Spanish blockade and spent four years in Palestine. The radio had changed to the plaintive strains of *Harbour Lights*. The train came and he was gone. Had he ever been?

Tomorrow, I must go back to hospital, but now I went to collect mother from her friend's house. It was a night of dangerous moonlight and we were half way home when the sirens began to wail; their high-pitched lamentations always exhilarated me strangely and I felt guilty because of it. There was no available shelter ahead, but mother would never retrace her steps. It was bad luck to turn back!

First, came the incendiary bombs, illuminating the landscape and drawing raiders in their wake like moths to the flames. The ominous drone of aircraft was followed by the crunch of heavier bombs and from the searchlight batteries, fingers of light probed the sky, trapping within their beams a tiny silver 'plane.

The ack-ack guns began a clangorous chatter and shrapnel spattered metallically around us.

Mother paused, just long enough to put up her umbrella.

In no time at all I knew that I was pregnant. I shared out the stockings and resolved to hide my condition as long as possible. It was not easy; I was the only married member of the community and under constant surveillance by the others. Wally-bags speculated openly and asked impertinent questions, for her sister had double-jointed twins and she considered herself an authority on the subject.

" Be japers! " she asserted, " Sure, it's plain on your dial, no need for a conspicuosis belliosis." In vain I protested I was,

89

in fact, losing weight.

"The slope before the bank!" declared Wally, and began knitting little pants because it was sure to be "a broth of a boy.'

By now, the red alerts were constant. During the last three weeks I was there we kipped uneasily in odd corners and never went to bed at all.

Sadly, for the last time, I said goodbye to the hospital. Halfway home, the train halted and we were told that no more trains would get through that night. There was no seating accommodation and with the stopping of the train the feeble lights were doughted and the heating discontinued. It was a long, cold night and bonded together by a common misery, we stamped about, blowing on our numbed fingers and awed by the terrible magnificence of the skies ahead. It was Coventry ablaze

When he heard of my redundancy, my father-in-law wrote from a remote village in Yorkshire suggesting that I might like to housekeep for himself and my young brother-in-law. He did not know what he was letting himself in for; I had no domesticity. But still, if I did not know how to cook, at least I knew how to treat them for indigestion! So, I went alone to the Dales and the Cock-Beck and Ilkley moor "ba' tat."

I was intrigued and delighted to find that they drank tea from colourful "pint pots" decorated with mottos; mine bore the legend:

> "Hear all, see all, say nowt,
> Eat all, sup all, pay nowt,
> An' when tha does owt fer nowt,
> Allus do it fer thissen."

But the caption on the back was more brief and to the point. "Take hod and sup," it instructed, and so I did.

In the village, where everyone knew everyone else, I was vetted, dissected and reassembled with the precision of experts and the housewives hastened to disclose the dedicated doctrine of making Yorkshire pudding. It preluded every midday meal on a plate of its own and consecrated with rich gravy.

They all spoke like telegrams, missing out the little words and the "Co'op" was their religion. I once saw a van bearing the slogan: "Bury by the Co'op and collect the Divi!"

Most of the men worked in the pits, except my brother-in-law who was apprenticed out in Leeds. Pop-in-law, who was delighted by the prospect of becoming a grandparent, was in charge of the pit ponies; lovingly, he doctored and groomed them and saved tit-bits to take with his ' snap.' It was a sad day if he had to use the " humane killer " and his snap came back unopened. During the holiday period when the ponies were brought above ground for a brief spell, he would take us to see them cavorting in the fields, kicking up their legs, delirious with joy to feel the green grass and the sunlight.

I soon chummed up with the local district nurse who did just about everything. Trained nurses were hard to come by and she was delighted to have help with her clinics and, when confinements were imminent, to be able to — pass on to me the colostomys, carcinomas and laying-outs — and also her own small daughter when she was called out nocté.

Meanwhile, iron gates and railings were commandeered to be smelted down for raw materials; wrapping paper was scarce and we embroidered white huckaback in which to collect our rations and vied with each other in the queues as to whose was the whitest. I yearned for fresh fruit, but it was unobtainable; ships had more important cargoes than oranges for fanciful females. Tomatoes, when procurable, were seven shillings a pound. We were told to extract the juice from raw swedes, gather rose hips in season, and it was hinted that if we consumed raw carrots we would see better in the blackout!

My daughter was born on May the fifteenth, seven years to the day on which I had set out on my career. It was the first time I had been in hospital on the wrong side of the blanket. I had not heard from Gun-layer for several months and it transpired later that he was part of a skeleton crew that had been transferred to a German prize ship and then lost trace of. (Pop-in-law sent him a wire announcing his daughter's arrival, but she was nine months old when he finally received it!)

War news was despondent and there was talk of invasion. Hitler had a secret weapon. A deadly dysentery was rampant amongst the new born. What a heritage! I looked down at my little bundle. It was a bleak world I had brought her into; a missing father, an irresponsible mother, no hope of a home for years to come.

Then I cheered up again. After all, I thought, it's not everyone who can trace their beginnings to a spanner in the turbines!

5.

Now the years had evaporated. After nearly a quarter of a century of district nursing my retirement was in sight. So many patients had come and gone, as beneficial to me as I had been to them for we shared each other's joys and sustained each other in grief.

Mrs. Tibbs was still with me, rather dunny and decrepit, but far more knowledgeable. Television had re-educated her.

She rented her set from a firm who let out their older models at a minimal charge to old-age pensioners. This was a marvellous idea, for people like Mrs. Tibbs did not want BBC 2. She already fretted that two programmes ran simultaneously, and would willingly have sat up all night if they could have been played out separately.

She viewed everything, from Andy Pandy to the Archbishop of Canterbury; became an expert on racing, reviled politicians to their faces and celebrities became her personal friends.

She had also acquired the services of a home help, but the home help supervisor was hard put to accommodating her, for she constantly waged war with the ladies and many departed in distress, refusing ever to " do " for her again.

Miss Price, the latest recruit, was a maiden lady of tact and determination. She pursued her job with a one track mind and a deaf ear, and for a while peace reigned. Of course, it could not last. Mrs. Tibbs began accusing her of filching some

of her allotted time in order to spend longer with Mr. Cutts, two
doors away.

"Anythin' ter git a mon!" she reviled and made lewd
insinuations, though the fact that Mr. Cutts was ninety-four,
hardly made him eligible for what she had in mind.

Finally, she refused to sign Miss Price's time sheet. It was
the last straw and once more the supervisor's help was enlisted.
This time she would stand no nonsense. "I'm sorry, Mrs.
Tibbs," she said firmly, "But I shall have to cut Miss Price's
time to one hour a day only!"

"Daze yer 'ide!" cried Mrs. Tibbs, outraged. "Why, 'ers
in an' out like a bloody fart in a colander!"

The supervisor retreated in high dudgeon. "Sod 'er!"
cried Mrs. Tibbs, unrepentant.

After this, Mrs. Buggins from next door started coming in
to perform small services. She was an unassuming little woman,
slow and fumbling, but with the use of her legs, which was what
Mrs. Tibbs lacked. Together, they made one functional body.
Mrs. Buggins shopped around for the cheapest cuts from the
butchers and would trudge a mile to save a penny. Shopkeepers
knew her and she had priority for broken biscuits, over-ripe
bananas and squashed cream cakes. It all saved chewing and
neither had a surfeit of gnashers. The two rejoiced together
over each small economy. Mrs. Tibbs' diet improved, and with
it, her temper.

In return for these benefits, Mrs. Tibbs invited Mrs. Buggins, who was televisionless, to share her viewing. After all, it
halved the lighting and firing. The two old ladies sat watching
until close down. It was in the days of the epilogue; they enjoyed that, said Mrs. Tibbs, it saved them saying their prayers.
It was so nice too, to say "good night" to the Queen, though
as Mrs. Tibbs said, "It's a cryin' shairm the way they keep that
poor wench up 'til all hours with 'er crown on."

Mrs. Tibbs lived in the shadow of the church and she
yearned to be embraced by its charity, indifferent to the fact
that the vicar had many demands on his time and bounty. She
considered that, as she had never been a church-goer, and now
because of her disabilities never could be, the favours of the
prodigal should be conferred on her with a generous helping
of the fatted calf

It rankled to see from her window the vague comings and

goings of the clergy to occasions from which she herself was ostracized. She thought longingly of bun fights and jumble sales and was mortified by the injustice of it all.

I was late gettting to her one day, but regardless of this, I could see she had got one on her. " Parsons! " she spat with venom, " Fartin' about in them capes like bloody batmen, lettin' the ode folks goo ter pot! Arr well, if the Lord doh come 'e sends. Yo' allus turn up, even if yo' bin as be'ind as the cow's tael."

" I am late," I admitted. " Got landed with a laying out."

This immediately took her mind off thankless theologians and while I administered to her there was a catechism on the departed one. She knew everyone and took great satisfaction in seeing old associates pass on.

Still anxious to avoid the vicar, I directed her thoughts to television. " Did you enjoy the film last night? " I asked.

" I dey see it," she replied, adding self righteously, " I 'ad me bath in front 'o the fire instead."

" But you could have watched the film while you were having your bath! " I protested.

" What! " she cried, scandalised. " An' let them see me! "

" They say as 'ow our nus is retirin'," volunteered Mrs. Buggins one day. " Well, 'er'll still cum ter we," responded Mrs. Tibbs with confidence. She couldn't abide changes; there were far too many these days and not for the better. As for the telly! The things they taught the kids! She and Buggins had learnt more by watching school programmes than they had ever known in all their lives! And look at the meat. The poor beasts; if they were allowed to act naturally there would be plenty of meat. It was flying in the face of nature what they did nowadays; no wonder the beef was riffy. She didn't even fancy it any more; artificial, her foot!

She and Buggins had watched a farming programme one afternoon and they could not believe their ears. Why, the vet did it himself now, the dirty varmint! " I reckon," speculated Mrs. Buggins, " 'E mus' tek 'is trausers off an' tup 'em standin' up."

Then there was all these strikes, putting up the price ol everything except the old-age pension. First the miners, then the electricians, now all the factories were coming out. Mrs.

Tibbs was very truculent. I was glad to see the first signs of spring amongst the stunted shrubs in her back garden. Tiny yellow blooms were appearing on the bare branches, that would cheer her up.

"Forsythia's out!" I announced, breezing in.

"God a'mighty!" exploded Mrs. Tibbs, "Another soddin' strike?"

* * *

"Henery," another long term patient, was a large lethargic man whose legs, weary of supporting his cumbersome frame, had "broke out" in protest. I dressed them daily and bound them with crepe bandages and once a week, assisted by Mrs. Henery, I gave him a bath.

Henery spent most of his days sitting in the ingle nook of their little cot and said nowt about owt. His wife, though her attitude towards me was always friendly, brooked no interference with her spouse, and when I suggested that exercise might stir his sluggish circulation, she wanted him to stay put. When I proposed more protein and less carbohydrate in his diet, she asserted that Henery must never eat red meat or cheese. She added darkly that Henery needed watching.

She always made a point of being present when I attended to him and when going shopping (she usually came in the car with me to get a lift), I noticed she was most careful, after securing the fireguard, to lock him in.

Also, she was very wary of visitors and always answered the door with her hat on. If the visitor was welcome, she had just come in, but if they were unwelcome, she was just going out.

The old-age pension does not cater for extras, and so when Mrs. Henery sighed that their blankets were getting threadbare, I said not to worry, I was sure the social security would help, and I would get them to send a welfare officer.

A few days later, I was amazed, on approaching Henery's home to see a little red mini parked outside and a vision of loveliness emerging from his front door, the dolliest of dolly-birds! Pale gleaming shoulder length hair swung freely round her piquant little face and a minuscule mini-skirt displayed her shapely limbs to perfection. Dimpling endearingly, she waved a farewell, swung her supple self into the mini car and roared off down the road.

I stood open mouthed for some moments before seeing Mrs. Henery, arms akimbo, astride her front doorstep.

" Got yo' ter thank fer that! " she called belligerently.

This was not like Mrs. Henery; I hastened to find the cause. " That young beesom," she nodded in the direction into which the creation had disappeared like a mirage. " Welfare werker! " she spat out the words with venom.

" What, her? " I cried ungrammatically. To me, " welfare worker " conjured up a homely little man with baggy pants and a black note book. Things had certainly changed! " I'm sure she's qualified," I said lamely.

" Qualified fer what? " snarled Mrs. Henery, standing aside for me to enter.

I noticed then that there was something strange about Henery. He was lumbering about restlessly and when he saw me, he took my hand and led me to a chair. I sat down, for it was obvious that he had something momentous to impart. His eyes were glazed and he was sweating slightly when he spoke, slowly but clearly.

" It's bin a long time since I 'ad it." I looked to Mrs. Henery for explanation.

" 'E's torkin' abart that wot yo' cor ate! " she snapped. She sat down heavily in the chair opposite and sighed. " It's 'er, that fancy wench, 'er's set 'im off agin. Strokin' 'is 'ond an' pattin' 'is yed an' 'im agawpin' saft as shit! The braizen 'ussy, showin' 'er arse an' all! Dun yo' know, when 'er sot theer, wheer yo' bin," she leaned forward confidentially and added in a hoarse whisper, " I sid 'er gusset! "

Hastily I crossed my legs, though I doubted my directoire knickers would arouse any lust in Henery's breast.

" Yo' ring that welfare an' tell 'em niver ter send 'er 'ere agin, bugger the blankets! " She sighed again. " I'm agooin' t'ave such a gairm wi' 'im agin. I'll be wishin' I'd got me 'onds on 'er ternight! "

I didn't say, but it struck me that Henery would be wishing the same thing.

*   *   *

My daughter looked at me speculatively and said, " You know, I think an eyeliner would help you." I was rather taken aback. I had not realised that I needed help, but mostly I was gratified to find that someone still took an interest in my appearance. The next time I went to the chemists, at the end of my miscellaneous list, I added " eyeliner."

The dear man looked rather perplexed by my unusual request, for my purchases are normally limited to catheters, lubricants and glycerine suppositories.

" Eyeliner, nurse? " he questioned, scratching the back of his head (I have quite a rapport with chemists and undertakers which I realise is stimulated by my profession rather than my own peculiar type of charm).

" Eyeliners now, not much in my line." He laughed nervously at his own little pun. " Perhaps we should get one of the girls."

" Oh no! ' I protested (Dolly birds diminish me), " I'll find it myself."

I rummaged amongst the alien goods on his counter until I found eyeliners. Apparently, there was a choice; either a plain black pencil or else a small bottle of black liquid to which was attached a fine camel hair brush. I settled for the liquid — painting is my hobby — and I had taken a fancy to the camel hair brush.

I made a quick escape, thankful that my purchase had not been observed by some joker. My friend the chemist still looked anxious. I could hardly wait to try out my new beauty aid and as soon as I reached home I closeted myself in the bathroom and, still hampered by my hat, endeavoured to follow the directions. " With the brush, paint a line as near as possible to the lashes," they instructed. This called for time and concentration and a very steady hand, but before long someone was clamouring to get in and hurriedly I washed it all off.

The following morning, with quite a youthful stirring in my blood, I rose at five-thirty and, when my usual chores were done, settled down in the fierce light of the kitchen to do justice to my face. I'm forty plus (Oh well then, fifty plus!) and my eyelids tend to wrinkle, not at all conductive to painting on. However, I thought the general effect was quite pleasing, if just a little bog-eyed. I could hardly wait to try myself out and escaped while the family were fresh from their beds and too bleary eyed to take notice of me.

The diabetics were my first concern; their need for insulin is urgent and they are given priority on the visiting list. Until she has got them out of her hair, a district nurse does not consider her day has begun.

The first patient was of such long standing, she qualified as an old friend. Half closing her eyes, she regarded me with compassion. " Yo've bin called out in the night agin, I con see. It's a cryin' shairm, yo' look 'arf jed! " I did not stay any longer than was necessary.

The second patient made no comment; he was very short-sighted but he asked if I would take his prescription to the chemist whose shop lay en route to the next patient.

My friend, the pharmacist, was openly amused. I could not bring myself to return his amiable grin and my confidence was fast deteriorating. While he dealt with the prescription, the entire staff emerged each in turn from their inner sanctum, obviously to view me. I detected giggling amongst the dolly birds.

Shouting that I would return later for the prescription, I made a confused exit. The chemist was no longer my friend, worse still he was disloyal. In future I would take my custom elsewhere and with it, all those lucrative prescriptions that patients asked me to collect. Comforted by thoughts of revenge, but with my ego deflated, I stumbled into the kitchen of patient number three.

She took one look and embraced me.

" Doh tell me! " she cried, " Yo'n got one o' yer 'eads agin. I con allus tell be thee eyes. 'Ow abart a cuppa char? Or," (in a conspiratorial whisper, though no one else was within earshot), " 'ow abart a wet? " As a female body living alone, she was earmarked by us all as a convenient pennyhouse and she glorified in being the chosen.

" No thank you, dear," I said, as I disengaged myself and made for the sink, " but there's some mud in my eye. Could I possibly have a little swill? "

The camel hair brush is very useful.

*   *   *

" It is better to dwell in a corner of the house-top, than with a brawling woman in a wide house," counsels Proverb chapter 21, verse 9, and is so sure of the sagacity that it repeats itself four chapters later.

Old Eli dwelt in a corner of the house-top under the eaves well away from the wide house which was really his, and from the brawling woman who was his daughter-in-law. It is soul destroying to be old and unwanted, and he waited hopefully to be reberthed in a home for the aged. He was a mild little man but the meek are not always blessed and his contemporaries who were less quiescent, potched him every time.

The brawling woman commandeered his pension to pay for his miserable gas fire and the fodder she begrudgingly dolloped out for him, and I attended to give him injections for anaemia which was not improved by the aforesaid fodder.

In the yard, a very off-putting mongrel dog trailed its chain through the putrefying accumulation of its own excreta, and responded to my overtures of friendship with a savage snarl and a menacing curl of the upper lip. I had always before been able to win over the most belligerent of the canine species, but I never trust one that is tethered, for the strength of a chain lies in its weakest link and one day that link will surely sever.

When I broached the subject of the dog to Eli's daughter-in-law, she snorted that the creature had never been loosed; only her spouse dared to approach it and then only armed with a goad! Poor brute, no wonder it waged a vendetta with homo-sapiens.

There was also a scrawny cat, munched and scarred and lumpy with kittens. One day, it was keening sadly and its progeny obviously gone — " In bucket! " bellucked the woman, " Same as all the t'others! " Later, I found the cat in a corner of Eli's garret, mewling over one of his knotted old socks and proffering dugs rich with wasted milk. The next time it was in kit, I asked if one could be saved for me; the cat should have some joy in its barren life and maybe in future I could canvas for homes to save one from each litter. Out of her very mean-ness, the brawling woman balked, so I offered to take on the job of emptying Eli's commode to appease her.

As the births were imminent, I provided a box lined with woollies. The woman would not tolerate it in the house, but I established it in a corner of the large outside loo and baited it with tit-bits brought from home, so that the cat accepted it. I was rewarded, for one morning she lay suckling a solitary kitten and the warm brown sound of purring was a hymn of thanksgiving.

She knew three weeks of fulfilment and then it happened. I had just emptied Eli's commode in the closet when the weakest link snapped and the dog hurtled towards me. I tried to face

99

it, keeping Eli's receptacle between us, but the beast circled me, snarling, and in doing so, twined the length of the chain which was still attached to its collar, round my legs. I tottered and fell. There was no escape for we were bound inexorably together and the brawling woman had perfidiously slammed shut the back door, with herself on the safe side of it! The brute slavered over me, its saliva dripped on to my face when, with an unearthly scream, the cat, like a bat from hell, landed on its head. In the ensuing holocaust, I freed my legs from the entanglement of the chain and the dog, howling, hared down the road leaving the poor broken body of the cat dead upon the fode.

I did not reproach the woman for infidelity but humbly, for I feared a refusal, asked for the kitten. In its defence, the mother cat had indebted me too.

We fed the tiny bumbling creature with milk from a doll's bottle and soft red pulp scraped from the surface of raw beef, and bedded it with a whippet who brooded over it with loving care and croodled the little orphan within the circle of his long body, cleansing it meticulously. When it was grown into a lordly Tom, it reciprocated by warming his old bones on winter nights.

*　　*　　*

It is inevitable that one becomes involved with the animals of a house when frequenting it. Sometimes, when there was a litter of pups, I was compromised into docking their tails if the breed demanded that mutilation (though never in the company's time!) Recollecting Cloggy, a familiar of my earlier schooldays, it even seemed kinder to do it than to leave it to some hamfisted Tom, Dick or Harry who might botch the job.

Cloggy was as sinister a character as you could hope to meet in a month of Sundays and he lived with a witch. She might have been his mother or even his wife. Cloggy was of indeterminate age, but certainly the old gammer was a witch, for she was wall-eyed and toothless, and her curved beak and upturned chin almost met. In their backyard, a long-handled birch broom leaned drunkenly against the wall, obviously for nocturnal transport, and as we passed en route for school, we crossed our fingers and spat over them as a proviso against the occult.

Cloggy himself was a pied piper who drew children magnetically in his wake, for he was an odd-job man with a bent for the macabre. He dug graves and cesspits, disposed of rejected pets, wrung the necks of chickens destined for the pot, and docked puppy dog's tails. He was a familiar figure, trailing a reluctant dog on a string in the direction of the cut, an ominous brick in his hand.

Our classroom window was purposely designed to thwart the wandering eye, but Cloggy had a gammy leg and his ungainly gait, accentuated by hobnailed boots, identified him so that when he passed we stirred resentfully, speculating on where he might be going without us. Our teacher, " Catty-white-drawers," who also recognised the hoppity-hop, would rap smartly for attention.

There was an outcry recently on the radio (my current source of news), against tail docking. I never seem to get down to reading newspapers until they are spread on the deck under the dog's dishes; we are such stuff as fools are made of and our beasts dine on the hearthrug. If they have ever been so inauspicious as to find their pampered paws in communication with cold kitchen tiles, they have been known to tow their fittle to a more propitious position.

Once so debased, the newsprint becomes irresistably desirous, and I crawl around on all fours avidly absorbing information which other folk have long since forgotten, commenting waspishly on the inevitable floosies who flaunt their privy parts with boring abandonment. Weeks after the event, news has assumed its rightful proportions, speculating journalists have lied in their teeth and the chicanory of politicians is laid bare. If the anti-dockers made the headlines, I have not yet caught up with them, but it matters not, the radio campaigner converted me. I am a sucker for conversion, changing my religion and politics at the drop of a hat, and all the tiny tails which I have nipped off with clippers, applying a swab of Friar's Balsam to the sad little stump, hang heavily on my conscience.

Cloggy was less clinical. The word soon got around if any local bitch had whelped, and unless it was of the long tailed breed (and most were of the Heinz variety), we knew that in a few days the gruesome ritual would be enacted. Cloggy worked better with an audience and would ivver-ovver until there was a suitable assemblage. We responded by making a feast of the performance and congregated with such sustenance as tiger nuts, bulls eyes, gobstoppers and long brown locust

101

beans, the sweet pod of the carob, resembling dried banana skins but really quite delicious.

When all was hushed and still, except for a satisfactory sucking and the frequent inspection of gobstoppers which underwent many colour changes before reaching the tiny seed in the centre, Cloggy commenced. Then all sucking ceased, and our toes curled in horrific anticipation.

Selecting one of the unfortunate pups laid sacrificially before him, Cloggy would put the tiny creature to his mouth and manipulate the minute vertebra of its tail between his teeth. The hapless pup scriggled in vain, there was a scrunch, an agonised screak and yammering grievously, it was discarded for the next victim, while the boys jostled for the tail spat out by Cloggy, and the girls recoiled with feminine delicacy.

When the executions were over, Cloggy would clear his throat raspingly, eject a great gob of phlegm and then, delicately taking his nostrils between thumb and forefinger (and diplomatically turning his back to the wind), blew his nose into the gutter.

The mother of the litter was always secured at the onset, but on one occasion the bitch, a sharp little terrier, broke loose just as he was operating on one of her offspring and Cloggy, being rather dunny, didn't hear her coming until she sank her teeth into his unwary buttock. His sharp intake of breath was calamitous, for the tail he had just bitten off went down the wrong way and despite much hawking and wambling and thumping on the back, it refused to be dislodged.

The effect on Cloggy was traumatic; he never performed again with the same aplomb and soon joined the fraternity of night-soil men which conveniently put him on the same shift as his witch.

This morning, on the radio, there was a stir among humanists to protect the modern child from the potential dangers of horror on the box!

Mrs. Tibbs put on both pairs of her specs, one behind the other, and settled down to read the previous evening's local paper which I had just left with her. She did not mind her news second-hand since it was for free, and on alernate Fridays Mrs. Buggins took the accumulated papers to the fish-and-chip shop and exchanged them for chips which, doused with vinegar, they found very tasty.

Her main interest lay in births, marriages and deaths; " hatches, matches and dispatches " she called them, and by keeping a record of the " matches " on her calendar she was able, at a later date, to team them up with the " hatches " and get some interesting results. Not that marriage rated very high in her estimation, her own having ended abruptly after less than a year when her ill-fated spouse, after a night out with the boys, had fallen down a pit shaft and broken his neck. Simultaneously, she had miscarried and had never been tempted to repeat the experience. Wedlock, she reckoned, was " Nowt more'n fower legs inna bed," adding laconically that " the fust three months yo' could ate it, an' the nex' three months yo' wish yo' 'ad! "

Now, skimming the columns of the paper, an advertisement caught her eye; ' Free range eggs,' at a place in Gornal. Already she saw them, smooth and brown with deep yellow yolks and whiter than white whites. Her mouth began to water. She hammered on the wall and Buggins came in at a trot, whereupon they speculated like financial wizards and decided the bus fare was justified.

" S'truth! " cried Mrs. Buggins when learning her destination. " Gornal! That's wheer they put the pig on the wall ter watch the band goo by! "

" Then mind they do' put yo' on the wall! " snapped Mrs. Tibbs, who could never resist an insult. But it was wasted on Mrs. Buggins, who was beginning to get quite excited — she hadn't been so far abroad for years and felt like a pioneer. She donned her best gear, the red plush hat with cherries on it (twopence from a jumble sale), the black out-dated astrakhan coat (from the same source), and her boots. She always wore men's lace-up boots since they were so accommodating for her bunions. Mrs. Tibbs had the foresight to furnish her with the newspaper cutting and she stuffed it in a worn purse which had seen much service, if little cash. Thus equipped, she sallied forth, her string bag completing her kit.

When the bus came, she walked its length and took a back seat under the impression that by doing so she got a longer ride; it was a long time before the conductor reached her, and when he did she squawked protestingly at the fare he demanded.

"I aye bin on a buzz fer years, I air gorrit! " she persisted. (She certainly did not have enough for both ways and on the return trip she would be lumbered with the eggs). Reasoning that every moment took her further on her way, she kept up the repartee so that by the time the conductor had stopped the bus and ejected her, she was much nearer to her destination, but it was still a very long tramp. Now, she had to keep asking the way; it was amazing the number of folks who didn't know where they were themselves. She kept offering them her bit of newspaper with the address on it, for not for anything would she admit that she could not read. She had never had much time for schooling, though she could tot up with the best of them. It took a ' fast one ' to diddle her!

Her ma had taken in washing and every day had been a wash day; as the eldest, it was she who rose early to light the fire under the brick-built copper; she who did the maiding with the heavy wooden maid nearly as high as herself, crying over her broken chilblains on a winter's morning, and many the clout she got up 'er lug 'ole fer bein' a quiddler! What a stir it had caused amongst the women when the first soap-powder came out. *Hudsons*, it was. They said it would never catch on, but now look!

Pa had been a puddler; it was hard graft puddling iron, and the blast furnaces lit the night skies with a ruddy glow. Pa came home weary to death and always thirsty for his beer; lively enough he was abed, though, and had a brood to prove it. Every year brought a new brother or sister. Once it was twins and they used to give them a sugar rag dunked in Laudanum. That kept 'em quiet! A rare smile creased her face and grimly she plodded on.

Back home, Mrs. Tibbs fretted for her tea. Just fancied one of them fresh eggs, she did. Wherever had old Buggins got to? Her belly rumbled in protest at the delay and in the end she made do with " drippin' toast." The silly old faggot must have got lost.

When she finally got back, Mrs. Buggins had a defeated look and appeared to have diminished in size. " Wheer's th' eggs? " demanded Mrs. Tibbs.

" I aye got none," lamented Mrs. Buggins. She was weary, famished, and moreover, she had missed *Crossroads.*

" Bloody chates! " she ejaculated, injustice rising like bile in her craw. " When I ast 'em fer range eggs, the buggers

104

waented five bob a dozen! The soddin' liars! They wor' free
at all! "

*   *   *

After the debacle of the eggs, Mrs. Buggins was very subdued. " Got the sulks," decided Mrs. Tibbs and ignored the
whole affair. After all, she had suffered too; she had really
fancied a nice brown country egg — you could not get decent
eggs these days. Not that you could blame the hens; what could
you expect from poor things that ran off batteries. Her wireless
worked off a battery and half the time she could not get anything out of it.

Mrs. Buggins had other fish to fry, however, and was busy
preparing herself. Once more she unearthed her astrakhan coat
and skewered the red plush hat to her bun with a long pin.
' Doll,' her daughter, had ostracised her for years, but now, seeing that her mother's company was sought elsewhere, to wit by
Mrs. Tibbs, sought a reconciliation. After all, you have
only one mother; also, she herself now had three children and
could do with a baby sitter. When she was asked to ' sit-in,'
Mrs. Buggins was very flattered and very willing.

" Wheer bin yo' agooin'? " demanded Mrs. Tibbs suspiciously, when she appeared with her hat on.

" I'n agooin' t' our Dolls," announced Mrs. Buggins, " ter
mind the kids while 'er an' Perce goos ter the pitchers."

" I shud think yo' bin! " cried Mrs. Tibbs. " If yo' goo
theer abumsuckin' yo' waent yer yed lookin'. Yo' bay all theer."

" I bin as I bin an' if I bay I bissent! " retorted Mrs. Buggins defiantly, making her exit with all the dignity she could
muster.

" Red 'at an' no breeches! " Mrs. Tibbs hurled the final
insult after her. " Goo an' jiy goo wi' yer! "

When Mrs. Buggins appeared on her daughter's threshold,
Doll dragged her hastily inside before the neighbours caught
sight of her. Those boots! And that hat! Quickly, she divested
her mother of her outer garments.

Mrs. Buggins wore a clean pinafore over her jumble-sale
jumper. " Take your pinny off, ma," begged Doll. " You
haven't come to work! " she added gaily, until in detaching her
mother from the offending garment she revealed the threadbare
skirt underneath. " Never mind," she compromised, tying it
back on, " you can do the washing up."

105

Already, she regretted the reunion. Percival had been very much against it having congratulated himself on being mother-in-law-less, and not anxious to be lumbered with one at this late stage.

The twins, Mandy and Marilyn and their little brother, Errol, already pyjamad, supped and well washed behind the ears, were watching television. They could stay up until the end of their programme, said Doll, and admonished them to behave for grandma. She was anxious to get Percival out of the house before he made contact with mother and hastened their departure for this reason. She left a snack in the kitchen in case her mother got peckish, and was gone.

No sooner had their parents departed than Marilyn began twiddling the television knobs to change the programme. " Ee, yo' moent dew that! " cried Mrs. Buggins anxiously, for to her television was a time bomb adjusted only by Mrs. Tibbs.

" It's our telly isn't it? " snapped Mandy, quick to defend her twin.

" Why yo' cheeky little sod! " screeched Mrs. Buggins, who came from the era when children were seen and not heard.

Marilyn sniffed and remarked loftily, " Somebody has let off." Then all three children stared pointedly at their grand-mother who made a defeated and confused exit.

In the kitchen, she found on a tray, a hunk of pork pie, tomatoes, a slice of apple-tart and a bottle of stout. She would enjoy them better at home, so she wrapped them up and transferred them to her bag. No good letting them go to waste. Then she went in search of the toilet. She soon tracked it down; it had ' Private ' painted on the door in large letters, but she couldn't quite make it out and thought it stood for ' Privy.'

It was a toilet-cum-bathroom; the bath and toilet were in matching pink, as were the bath-mat and a mat surrounding the pedestal, beside which was a plastic container for a plastic pink lavatory brush. Doll, she remembered, had always favoured pink. The colour scheme was relieved by blue plastic curtains and a row of birds in full flight, and in decreasing sizes, affixed to the far wall. Even the Queen, decided Mrs. Buggins, could not have bettered this.

Later, she made a tour of the bedrooms and enjoyed having a good moach. It was all very impressive; Doll, she decided with satisfaction, had done well for herself. The connubial bed

106

in particular attracted her; it looked so comfortable and irresistibly inviting to her poor old feet. She loosened her boots and lay down on it, pulling the pink satin quilt over herself. In no time at all, she was asleep.

When Doll and Percival returned they were scandalised to find the children watching the late-night movie. " But we're granny sitting! " they cried defensively, and guttural snores from above stairs substantiated their claim.

Mrs. Buggins trudged home in high dudgeon. What a shindig they had kicked up just because she was having a little kip on their bed, snotty-nosed buggers! She must never let Mrs. Tibbs know how right she had been, so decided to ignore their recent fracas and to offer the stout as a peace-offering.

Mrs. Tibbs was still up and accepted the stout graciously; reciprocating by taking out two mugs and pouring half in each. In return, Mrs. Buggins produced the pie and apple tart, and the two old ladies settled down to a midnight repast. When repleted, Mrs. Tibbs brushed away the crumbs; " Well? " she queried, indicating that a state of confidence had been reached, and Mrs. Buggins needed no second bidding. Mrs. Tibbs listened intently, deducting all she heard by half to allow for exaggerations, and Mrs. Buggins, knowing she would do this, overstated accordingly. Doll's home took on new dimensions; the telly became coloured and the rooms carpeted. The closet alone needed no codding; she enthused on the plastic curtains, the " flight o' swallers " on the wall, the pretty mats — " yo' cud ate off the floor! " and the pink lavatory brush.

" But mind yer, Tibbs," she reflected thoughtfully, returning to mundane matters. " I'd sooner 'ave a bit o' pairper mesen. S'truth! Them brushes doh 'arf scratch yer arse! "

* * *

My dislike of Sunday stems back to my childhood when I was made to attend Sunday school. I found Biblical stories unconvincing, and at an early age my inquiring mind made me unpopular. I was labelled stubborn, and to my humiliation the curate once prayed openly for me. Neither his prayers nor the years did anything to convert me, but by reason of age alone I graduated eventually to becoming a Sunday school teacher. This proved even more calamitous, unseemly hilarity in my class was criticised, and my unorthodox approach to religion was frowned on by my superiors.

Came the Sunday when I had to shepherd my little flock to church for a service by the Bishop. On coming out, they clustered in an excited group in the churchyard comparing coins. " 'Ow much an yo' got? Cor, on'y a tanner! I got tew bob! " and it was revealed that they had helped themselves from the collection plate under the impression that it was a magnanimous handout by the Almighty. I was now beyond the pale, and it was a relief to all except the children when my chosen career took me away from home and the religious guidance of the young was relegated to a more pious person.

Gremlins still pursue my Sabbath; when speed is essential, road works and abnormal loads dog my path; when speed is possible, rogue radar traps recriminate me. This was my week-end on duty alone. Nearly thirty daily visits was already increased by a trickle of new cases via the ambulance service. On Sunday morning, I set off at seven-thirty, starting off with priority visits (diabetics must needs be early risers!). Two enemas awaited me, both urgent, since hospitalisation depended on the results. Both were revealed to be impacted faeces necessitating manual evacuations. It was eleven o'clock before I began the routine work.

Meanwhile, I had developed a slow puncture and at intervals had to use my foot-pump on the offending tyre. It was late afternoon before I returned home for my husband to deal with it. Thank heavens for handy husbands! Five cases for penicillin awaited my attention and from then on it was obvious that 'flu was rampant amongst the immigrants. I groaned. Oh, the language problem. Communication must be established by mime. Imagine finding out whether or not a coloured patient has had his bowels moved!

The first three victims lived in the same tenement building. No response from the front door, so I tried the back. After a great commotion of bolts and creaking keys, the door was opened on a chain. I was inspected, drawn inside and the bolts shot back in situ. The guardian of the door pointed upwards; turbanned men of all shapes and sizes littered the floor on pallet beds. All eyes turned towards me as I stepped over them to reach the stairs. The second floor was similar; men lounging on the stairs pointed further upwards.

My patients, also on pallet beds, looked very ill indeed. I spoke gently, hoping at least the tone of my voice would reassure them. No water was available and I donned disposable gloves and prepared the injections; dark eyes following my every move with apprehension. Since it has been established that many people have an intolerance for penicillin and could collapse as a result, a trial dose is first given, the remainder being administered twenty minutes later if no ill-effects are apparent. In each case, the initial dose was borne stoically, but when I approached with the second, they reacted violently, wagging forefingers before my face to indicate one, only one! The second injection was imperative so that eventually, in desperation but ashamed, I gave it by brute force.

They lay back on their pallets resigned to a quick demise from what they were convinced was an overdose. The next four injections would be given by a different nurse, and since non-allergy was now established, only one daily jab would be necessary. I should be condemned as a novice out to practice on them.

When I descended the stairs a deputation awaited me. I was ushered into the kitchen and seated with reverence on the only chair. Obviously, they had been told that a cup of tea was the done thing. I was not allowed to escape without it. With horror I watched as the tea, sugar, milk and water were all deposited in the kettle and boiled together. Only when I had consumed a cup of the scalding result did the guardian of the door produce his keys and I was bowed out with much ceremony.

The next two patients were more difficult to locate — I had been given the wrong address. Conditions were much the same as in the previous house and their reactions to the second jab even more protesting. I left depressed and with a feeling of professional inadequacy. Outside, I found my husband seeking me; three more immigrants had been 'phoned in and he wished to save me the journey home.

Once more the potential patients shared the same address and on my way there an ominous red light appeared on the dashboard indicating that my battery was not charging. The evening work would have to be done via my husband's motor cycle. The new patients lived in a more affluent area where the houses were old but elegant and had ' class.' The house for which I searched was immediately obvious since it flaunted a frontage of violet and pea green, a screaming comparison with the sombre black and white of its neighbours. It was also furnished, and in each room, visible through the open doorways, men demonstrated their culinary arts over gas rings, frying pans were flourished and an odour of curry and spice pervaded the air. On seeing me, several came out and smilingly gesticulated towards a closed door. I knocked and was admitted to a room where three people were clustered round a paraffin heater; there was a very handsome woman, a man, and a most beautiful child of about seven years. The child had the face of a cherub, her huge dark eyes were fringed with long sweeping lashes, and her black springy curls fell to below her waist. The colourful garments accentuated her dusky charm and I longed to portray her on canvas.

None of the occupants looked ill, but they produced vials of penicillin to substantiate their claim. I prepared the injection and the man obligingly proffered himself, but the woman intervened and loosening her clothing, arranged herself gracefully on the bed. I consulted my instructions, Mrs., it was! She accepted both injections with the satisfaction of a woman who felt she was getting value for money. Mollified, I admired the child who seemed to comprehend a little; children were usually the first to learn the new language. Patting her curls, I congratulated them on having so lovely a daughter. She was, I said, the most beautiful little girl I had ever seen. The parents, sensing a compliment, smiled and nodded graciously. The angel child made a very rude gesture. Rebuffed, I went in search of the next patient.

He lay on a bed which shook beneath him, whether with fear or a rigor I was not sure. I made soothing noises and turned away to make my preparations. When I returned to the bed it was empty, as was the room. I peered under the bed and from its sanctuary saucer eyes peered back at me. I squatted on the floor and made more soothing noises; he retreated out of reach and as I moved to the other side of the bed he shuffled back. I could dismiss him as having refused treatment, but that was admitting defeat. More important, he obviously needed antibiotics and would probably result in pneumonia without. Dispoiling my white apron, I shuffled bellywise after him and grabbed an ankle. Then his other foot jerked out, catching me on the nose, a prominent proboscis, and blood gushed forth over both of us! Shuffling back from under the bed, I dragged him

110

protesting loudly in my wake. As we emerged, he arched his back, giving it a violent clout against the iron framework of the bed and bellowed with pain. Quickly, I was astride him and exposing the sore area.

There appeared to be no damage and I applied a gentle massage. I am told that I have a soothing touch; gradually, under the influence he relaxed and lay prone under my kneading fingers. My nose had ceased to bleed. Mentally, I gauged the upper and outward quadrant of his buttock and the site of the injection. The prepared syringe in a disposable towel lay on the bed within reach. Quick as a flash, I reached for it and plunged the needle home. This time he got the lot, no second chance with him! A loud round of applause came from the doorway, where an audience had gathered unseen. Bloody, but unbowed, I helped him back to bed. I had adrenolin at the ready in case of a reaction, but he suffered no ill effects. I appeared to have come off worst and my conscience smote me, for never before had I given so unsterile an injection.

Making exaggerated motions of ablution, I confronted the little crowd in the doorway. One obligingly brought me a bowl of water with which I cleansed first my patient, then myself, taking off my apron and using the less gory parts as a towel. The sight of so much blood had sobered them all. There was no way of explaining to them that it was mine.

On the next floor, the last patient lay quietly in his bed, dark eyes surveyed me from a brown face. This time I would stand no nonsense. I smiled silently and went over to the window to prepare the dose. Looking down into the yard below, I saw the angel child urinating against a wall — at least that explained the rude gesture!

I returned to the bed determined to preserve my professional dignity and addressed him in a loud clear voice. " Doctor," I assumed the familiar stance adopted by his general practitioner, " want me," beating my chest, " give you," touching his, " needle! " With a flourish, I produced the syringe.

Incredulity passed over his face as he raised himself on one elbow. " Why," he said in astonishment, " can't you speak English?"

*　　*　　*

Mrs. Tibbs loved the Queen with a deep abiding devotion. When the National Anthem was played she would totter tremulously on to her rotting old appendages and if she didn't quite stand to attention, at least she stood.

One of the other few times when she ventured to stand was to piddle in her " po'." She found that standing facilitated micturition, and anyway, sitting on her chamber or bedpan was so " 'ard on 'er arse." Actually, her " po' " was a beautifully designed pewter pot from which her forbears had quaffed their ale. It was smooth, exquisitely symmetrical and most accommodating for her needs and held a good pint. The generously curved handle, embellished with vine leaves, was at just the right angle for arthritic old hands to grasp. It was a utilitarian treasure.

Sometimes, when she stood for the Queen, she used her po' at the same time, killing two birds with one stone, as it were. She was sure the Queen would understand — she was such a loving lady. But if it happened to be on the telly, she always took the precaution of draping her apron in front of her in case the Queen should chance to look her way.

Mrs. Buggins didn't share her friend's sentiments regarding royalty. Their Perce reckoned they oughter be done away with, but Mrs. Buggins wouldn't go quite that far. She would just settle for a nice dark dungeon in one of them castles, where Perce said they ate rump steak three times a day off gold platters (and had a stout afore every meal, she shouldn't wonder).

When a royal occasion was imminent, Mrs. Tibbs planned the day with the precision of an old campaigner and the house was, under her direction, made " spike and spoon and Bristol fashion."

Mrs. Buggins, preparatory to the Royal Silver Wedding, was cleaning the windows. " Doh clane th' outside," instructed Mrs. Tibbs. " We doh waent everybody gawpin' in. Just clane th' inside, soo as we can see out."

But Mrs. Buggins' mind was on other things. " Worrabaut fittle? " she posed the all important question.

They had dined off bread and " march on " with polony for the Investiture and it had lain cold and heavy on their bellies for long after. Both had been two-double with the colly-wobbles.

Mrs. Tibbs pondered for a long time, for the now inclement weather demanded more creature comforts than polony or pigs' pudden. Something to warm their cockles was indicated.

"Wee'n a' Groaty Dick an' good ahviers," she decided. "An' a drap of ode crater in we dishle o' tay." After all, it was a celebration and Buggins could prepare the Groaty Dick beforehand.

Mrs. Buggins spat on the window pane with great satisfaction and applied more elbow grease; the menu was right up her street.

The festal day dawned overcast and with a threat of "Queen's" weather. Mrs. Tibbs wore her best ganzy and stays under her black alpaca, the collar of which she secured with a heart-shaped brooch pierced by an arrow bearing the word, "Mizpah." The alpaca gaped at the waist, but she concealed the inadequacy under a new apron, and while she found the corsets very confining, pride must have a pinch so that she bore the discomfort stoically. Even Mrs. Buggins conceded to a clean pinafore, though she protected it with a coarse apron while attending to the Groaty Dick.

Mrs. Tibbs kept an expectant eye on the time, quite an acrobatic feat since the clock would only go when it was upside down. She was anxious not to miss anything and the tedious prologue served only as an appetiser for the more exciting moments to come.

"Time ter put the pitcher on, Buggins," she said at last, "an 'tek yer 'urden appund off fust. Yoh doh waent 'er ter see ya in that, dun yer?"

"Doh werrit, I bay that frowsty," objected Mrs. Buggins But she removed the offending apron before switching on.

"Our Perce 'as got a coloured telly," she boasted.

"Well I shore never 'ave a coloured 'un!" retorted Mrs Tibbs.

"Then ya betta keep yer trap shut," admonished her friend, "Or yo'll be 'ad up fer discriminatin'!"

After much preambulation, the programme at last got down to the objective of the occasion and the two old ladies were rewarded with the vision of a radiant Queen and her consort sailing across their screen. While waving gaily to the crowds, the royal couple still found time to exchange a secret smile.

"Ah . . . doh 'er 'arf luv 'im," breathed Mrs. Tibbs ecstatically. "'Er thinks the sun shines out of 'is arse, bless 'er."

"I doh like Annies' 'at!" scoffed Mrs. Buggins, "Bugger me, it's like an 'osses' tael on May day!"

" Well 'er likes 'osses doh 'er? " defended Mrs. Tibbs indignantly.

They dined in style during the banquet, despite the exalted company they shared. Mrs Buggins guttled voraciously, and Mrs. Tibbs eyed her with distaste. She herself was unable to do justice to the Groaty Dick because of the corsets which were now crippling her.

" Buggins! " she bellucked. " I'm clammed ter jeth. Coost git these 'ere stays off afore they strangulate me! Put telly off fust! "

" Strewth! Yoh bay 'arf gittin' a big fat swopson! " cried Mrs. Buggins, revealing the gap in the alpaca.

" Yoh need talk, yo'm as fat as a tunkey pig yersen,' retaliated Mrs. Tibbs. " Now stop thee gammitin' an' doh be ockerd! "

" Then odge up a bit, these tapes ay 'arf in a skrobble."

" Cut the buggers afore I kench mesen! " pleaded the victim and when it was done, she breathed a sigh of relief as her belly swelled to its normal rotundancy.

" I wonder why they calls 'em corsets? " contemplated Mrs. Buggins.

" 'Cos yoh cor sit in 'em ya gawby sod! " exclaimed Mrs Tibbs, amazed at her cronies' ignorance.

During the Queen's ' walk-about,' Mrs. Tibbs became very concerned. This was a new procedure and she leaned forward, anxiously scanning the crowds and exhorting the monarch to beware of any suspicious characters who might be snipers conspiring to take a pot-shot. In particular, she entreated for caution when a child handed the Queen a posy which might easily have contained a letter-bomb, and was quite beside herself when her warnings were so flagrantly ignored.

Mrs. Buggins, now that their meal was over, was getting bored. " It aye a patch off the Jubilee bunny-fire up Ockabonk," she reminisced, " wi' all them barrels up the sides an' Rory the Ranter askraekin' on top, 'til some keffle bunted 'im an' 'e fell yed fust inter a tar barrel. It wor 'arf a loff! " She sighed. " We wus young beesoms then, there wus our Poll in 'er straw boater, 'er what wed ' Flash 'arry.' Poor Poll, 'e wor' 'arf a nineter! "

" Arr," recollected Mrs. Tibbs wryly. " 'Er married the miskin fer the muck an' got pizened wi' the stink on it! " She was emotionally exhausted by now and would be thankful when it was all over and she could relax her vigilance.

"Thank God 'er's wum," she said at last. "I'm all dum-mucked up," and her head began to nod drowsily.

The Queen was back in her palace with all the milling crowds outside. "Three cheers for the Queen!" went up the cry.

"What's 'er waent wi' three?" chuntered Buggins, truculent to the end. "'Er con on'y sit on one cor 'er?"

*   *   *

Mrs. Tibbs had never been to the seaside and did not particularly want to go, but Mrs. Buggins had been several times, and so she found the omission intolerable. The local pub favoured by Doll and Percival had a trip to Southport every Easter Monday for the dependants of its patrons, and Perce said he could wangle a ticket for Mrs. Tibbs as well. It was for free and the coach could accommodate a wheel-chair at the rear. What was more, ten bob from "the Tote" was awarded to each participant. The ten bob clinched it, and Mrs. Tibbs accepted the offer.

It was a momentous decision and she was naturally apprehensive, but Mrs. Buggins, superior by reason of her previous experiences, gave a foretaste of the joys ahead. "We teks we aitins with we, an' a thumb bit fer the road. Theer's bingoo an' winkles an' whelks," (no mention of the sea at all!) "But cummin' wum's the best bit. 'Strewth, we doh 'arf goo acummin' back! Then we 'as time ter stop fer a good booze up an' sing-song."

Last year, however, there had been a proper shindig when Ida Flen (who, of course, was generally dubbed "Ode Yuck"), went adrift and they had to go back three pubs before they found her locked in a lavatory. Then, it had taken the local fire brigade and a couple of gins to get her out.

Mrs. Tibbs had no lavatorial problems; she would just take her pewter pot and Buggins could empty it for her. Even her Victorianna drawers with their conventional vent up the middle would prove no obstacle, and there would be no corsets to torment her this time!

Easter Monday was fresh and full of promise as Buggins trundled her in her wheel-chair up to the pub; both hung about with string bags and paper carriers, and the pewter pot safely secured with a bit of string to the arm of the chair. The ' chara ' was waiting, together with a group of their old contemporaries, several newspaper men and the big florid bloke who organised the trips. He was there, said Mrs. Buggins in a hoarse whisper, to get his " pitcher " in the papers. He was an O.B.E. and Perce said that stood for *Other Bugger's Efforts.*

As Mrs. Tibbs was the only passenger in a wheel chair, he was photographed handing her the ten bob and smiling down at her with his big plastic gnashers.

Mrs. Tibbs felt very important to be making the front page of the local paper and even more so when the men took hold o. her, chair and all, to swing her up into the rear of the coach. " It's praper Aiven Day! " she rejoiced, recalling her youth when Easter Monday was known as " Aiven Day," and men had the privilege of lifting womenfolk high into the air.

The newspaper men were so delighted they took her down again and had the photographer take another picture of her going up. That, they assured her, duly captioned " Aiven Day," would be the picture to make the front page! The O.B.E. looked very mumchance at being left out after getting up so early.

" That's potched 'im! " thought Mrs. Tibbs smugly.

It was a rorty ride to Southport; the old folk were all togged up and in fine fettle and the driver switched on a radio which added to the gaiety. During the infrequent halts when the others disembarked, Mrs. Tibbs was able to make use of her po' in privacy and to assess her future prospects. If only she could butter Buggins a bit, she might get to all those bunfights and jumble sales for which she hankered, in her wheel-chair. After all, people with good legs only got corns and bunions and wore out shoe leather.

When they arrived the others made a bee-line for bingo, but Mrs. Tibbs was impatient for her first sight of the briny and, resignedly, Mrs. Buggins wheeled her to the sea-shore. Once there, she gaped with dismay at the great expanse of beach terminating in the far horizon where earth and sky met in a seemingly endless line.

In *War at Sea*, a television series, there had been great waves with big ships bobbing up and down. " Wheer is it? " she demanded. " Theer's nowt 'ere but bloody saft sond! Strewth, theer's more wairter in the cut back wum! "

"Tide's out," reported Mrs. Buggins laconically. "I'n bin cummin' years an' I air never sid it!"

After pithering along the promenade, they made for the town and comforted themselves with fish and chips, hot and crisp and straight from the paper. They bought peppermint rock for Doll and Perce's kids, but most of the shops displayed tawdry trinkets, gewgaws and whigmaleeries at prices that made them guffaw. In a better part of the town they came across an antique shop in the big bay windows of which was a copper kettle. (Ten quid! And not a patch off the one Mrs. Tibbs kept on the hob) and bits of brass she wouldn't have given the house room. She thought of all her tranklements and bits of orange and blue Staffordshire china and decided they must be worth a packet.

While they stared a young man came out of the shop; proper posh he was, and had his eye on the pewter pot which dangled by its string from the chair handle. He took hold of it and fondled it with reverential wonder, exclaiming in admiration at the dull gleam of beaten pewter, sheeny with much handling. He was joined by an elderly man with a high domed forehead and an authoritative mien, who was also very impressed. Would she consider selling it? they asked, and went up to a staggering price when she continued to refuse. Mrs. Buggins nudged her painfully and screwed up her old fizog grotesquely in an effort to make her accept, but Mrs. Tibbs remained adamant. She reckoned if she played her cards right, she could have her cake and eat it.

It was her duty, said the older man, to see that her beautiful pewter was not lost to posterity for it was a thing of rare workmanship. "Yo' con 'ave it when I'm jed," compromised Mrs. Tibbs, provided the proceeds went towards her funeral expenses. Her bit of insurance (with great foresight, her mother had insured each of her offspring at birth for a penny a week), would provide only bare essentials, but it was her dearest ambition to be "hammered well down," and to have a nice white cross with "Zilla Tibbs, R.I.P." to mark the spot. She had a horror of being plonked down some place where they would never find her.

When she hinted at further paraphernalia "back wum," the young feller promised to call on her when he went to the antique fair. to value them and to make everything legal and hunky dory. Meanwhile, they provided Mrs. Buggins with a card to post if she should be took sudden. Buggins was mollified; there was nothing she enjoyed more than a good funeral.

"Bugger me, Buggins! We 'ad orter sid the say!" regretted Mrs. Tibbs as they made their way coachwards. They had no time to see if the tide was in but she was highly satisfied with the day's achievements. She had been very disturbed since the moon landing, for all her life she had clung to the simple beliefs of childhood and the ground was cut from under her feet or rather, the celestial abode from above her head, by the invasion into space. She had collared the curate on one of his cursory calls. "Aye yo'," she said, attacking him viciously before he could even warm his knees by the fire. "Now, wheer's that friend fer little childer above the bright blew sky? Wheer's them golden gates an' all them 'arps we'd gotta play? Yo'n bin coddin' we ya varmints. They day find none, did they?"

The curate had spouted some rigmarole about his Father's house having many mansions. What a whopper! Why, everybody knew his old man kept a pub at Gornal!

Never mind, she would be in safe keeping under a marble cross with her name and R.I.P. carved on it; they would know where to find her when the time came.

"Wot's R.I.P. stand fer?" queried Mrs. Buggins when they reached the chara'.

"Return If possible," explained Mrs. Tibbs patiently.

She still had faith in the Last Trump.

My paternal grandfather never shaved in his life; his luxuriant beard bears witness to this on his old election photographs. He was a local councillor, a Justice of the Peace and a prosperous farmer until he went to law over a small piece of his property and lost.

Being a man of principle and knowing himself to be in the right, he took it further, right into the House of Lords, but without success. He died a broken man, not from losing his affluence and that of his wife, Jemima, but from a soul destroying loss of faith in British justice.

During his lifetime grandad had done much for the local community. Sunday school treats, celebration bonfires, and what were probably the first youth movements were held in his shoulder-of-mutton field. He had an affinity for brass bands and it is said he could play most musical instruments with great skill.

He also started the first ambulance service in the district, providing a vehicle and horses from the farm, and farmhands, too, in lieu of ambulance men. Archaic! But they coped, as ambulance men still do, with every eventuality.

Even the vagaries of Mrs. Tibbs were not unsurmountable when she reluctantly had need of their services.

It was a real pea-souper, rimed with frost, the night Mrs. Buggins roused me to say that Mrs. Tibbs was blowing her whistle.

There had been several tragedies in the news when old people had fallen and died of exposure, presumably because they were unable to attract attention to their plight. Many suggestions had been put forward to safeguard against this and one was that aged persons living alone should be given a card, ' Nurse Required,' to put in the window in the event of such an emergency. The cards were even issued, but rarely used since most victims were unable to reach either the window or the card when the occasion arose.

Alarm bells were the next device to be considered, but these proved too costly, and anyway they would be just as inaccessible as the cards to anyone floored and on their back.

I had the temerity to suggest police whistles and approached the M.O.H. both verbally and in writing, but was told they were unsuitable. However, I went my own way, publicising my brain child and kitting out my most vulnerable patients with a lanyard round the neck to which a whistle was attached and so knotted that they could neither pull it off nor choke themselves, and was always on their person. I explained to neighbours, so that whistle blowing would be investigated. This was the first time that Mrs. Tibbs had need of it.

I had to break a small pane to unlatch the kitchen window and climb in. Mrs. Tibbs lay on her back like a beetle and just as helpless; her left hand was twisted under her at an abnormal angle, surely fractured, but otherwise she appeared to be suffering only from shock and cold. We managed to hoist her into bed and between blankets; the fire was out, but the bricks she always kept in the oven instead of hot water bottles were still very warm and we wrapped them in their flannel bags and put them in with her. I bound up her injured wrist, at which juncture she began to cuss heartily and we knew then she would

119

be all right. We all had piping hot cocoa, and Mrs. Buggins obligingly offered to sleep with her to keep her warm.

The next morning, Mrs. Tibbs was up as usual, established in her big chair. She had removed the trappings from her wrist, but it was obviously still painful. Both of her hands and wrists were so swollen and distorted with arthritis that it was difficult to ascertain the damage and I went away to 'phone her doctor. He was just off to an urgent call, but promised to see her later and, meanwhile, to arrange for an ambulance to take her for X-ray.

When I returned to Mrs. Tibbs and told her, she bucked like a startled horse. She had never been in hospital, but she was convinced that they were inhabited by fanatical surgeons lurking to experiment on the unwary. " If I'n broke me wriss," she haggled, " they'll a'me under gas an' then it's God knows what the varmints 'ull be up to! " Compresses of comfry, she insisted, would soon put it right.

At this point, the ambulance men arrived and it took our combined efforts to wheedle her into the vehicle, though she recovered sufficiently to hurl abuse at the small audience clustered round it and shook her good fist at me as a parting shot.

She was on my mind all morning, for I was really very concerned about her. She was now in her late eighties and no match for the modern medico. As soon as I could find the time I returned, but she was already home looking very smug and pleased with herself. Mrs. Buggins was out in the garden gathering comfry.

The offending wrist was not encased in plaster as I had expected it to be and there was a note confirming that there was nothing more wrong than chronic arthritis. I felt very guilty making all that fuss for nothing. Poor old girl, it had been such a needless ordeal for her.

" I'm sorry," I said apologetically. " You know, I really did think they would find that you had a fracture there."

" I dey," grinned Mrs. Tibbs toothlessly. " I gid 'em the wrong 'ond."

120

BLACK COUNTRY TERMS
— FOR THE UNITIATED

Ack Dum.—At once.
Ahviers.—Share.
Aive.—Heave.
Aiven day.—Easter Monday.
Aks.—Ask.
Appund.—Apron.
Backen.—To keep back.
Backerapper.—Explosive firework.
Bally.—Belly.
Bawk.—Confuse.
Belluck.—Bellow.
Beesum.—Pert young woman.
Bibble.—Pebble.
Blether yed.—A fool.
Blobmouth.—Indiscreet Person.
Bobowler.—Large moth.
Boffle.—To hinder.
Bonk.—Small hill. (Climbin' up the bonk o' forty.—Near middle age)
Bost.—Burst.
Broo'us.—Brewhouse.
Bunny fire.—Bonfire.
Bunt.—Jostle.
Buz.—Bus.
Cack.—Excreta.
Cag mag.—Gossip.
Camplin.—Gossiping.
Caggy.—Left Handed.
Caw.—Cannot.
Chicklings.—Pig's intestines.
Chimdy.—Chimney.
Chops.—Mouth.
Chunter.—To grumble.
Clammed.—Hungry.
Coddin'.—Joking.
Codge modge.—Rough work.
Cost.—Could you? (Thee cosn't.—You can't).
Croodle.—Huddle together.
Cut.—Canal.
Dishle o' tay.—Cup of tea.
Don 'and.—Expert.
Dunny.—Hard of hearing.
Dunderhead.—A Dolt or numbskull.
Fittle.—Food, Victuals.
Fizog.—Face, Visage.
Flen.—Flea.
Fode.—Fold, Yard (Back Yard).
Frowsty.—Dishevelled.

Ganzy.—Under vest.
Gammitin'.—Playing the fool.
Gammy.—Lame.
Gawby.—Simpleton.
Groaty Dick.—Groats and meat stewed together.
Gawp.—To stare open mouthed.
Guffaw.—Coarse laughter.
Guttle.—Gobble.
Ines.—Woman.
Ivver ovver.—Hesitate.
Keffle.—A lumbering fellow.
Kench.—To sprain.
Lampin'.—Thrashing.
Loff.—Laugh.
Munch.—Ill treat.
Mumchance.—Doleful, Dejected.
Miskin.—Privy.
" Marry the miskin fer the muck an' git pizened wi' the stink on it."
    —To marry for money and live to regret it.
Naither.—Neitner
Nairun.—None.
Nash.—Weakling.
Nerker.—Mischievous (Child).
Nineter.—A Tarter, A terrible fellow.
Node.—Knew.
Ockerd.—Awkward.
Odge up.—Move up.
Pail.—Beat.
Pither.—Potter about.
Potch.—To forestall or get the better of.
Plonk.—Put down.
Randy.—Big-mouthed.
Rantan.—Violent.
Racket.—Din or clamour.
Ranter.—Primitive Methodist.
Riffy.—Unclean, Crumby.
Rigmarole.—Long unintelligible story.
Rorty.—Satisfactory.
Saided.—Sated, Glutted
Sawny.—Simple.
Skrobble.—A tangle.
Snape.—Snub.
Splod.—Flat-footed.
Strumpet.—Prostitute.
Swopson.—Large, Heavy.
Tank.—Sharp blow.
Tarradiddle.—A fib or lie.
Tater.—Potatoe.
Togs.—Clothes.
Traipse.—To wander about aimlessly.
Tranklements.—Paraphernalia, Miscellaneous belongings.

Tunkey.—Fat pig.
Two double.—Doubled up with pain.
Wairter.—Water.
Werrit.—Worry.
Wamble.—Nausea.
Whigmaleerie.—A trinket or gewgaw.
Whopper.—Anything large, A monstrous lie.
Wonkey.—Shakey, Unsteady.
Wull.—Whole.
Wum.—Home.
Yammer.—To complain peevishly.
Yuck.—Itch.
Osilan Plumbi.—Swinging the lead (Latin).

BLACK COUNTRY SOCIETY PUBLICATIONS

Black Country Stories (Jokes and Sayings)

Freemans Black Country Folk.

The " Stourbridge Glass Industry " in the 19c.

A History of St. John's Church, **Tipton** (formerly St. Martin's).

" Clebak " in the Black Country (Cartoons).

Around the Black Country (selections from ' The Blackcountryman ').

West Bromwich before the Industrial Revolution. D. Dilworth.

A Capful of Nails. David Christie Murray (Novel of the Nail Trade in the 19c.)

Details from:—

The Secretary, 49 Victoria Road, Tipton, Staffs.

The Black Country Society

Local organisations come and go. Some are created to meet a temporary need or to fight for a transient privilege. The Black Country Society was formed to concern itself with three urgent and permanent difficulties concerning the region.

First, it was realised that many people both within and outside the area were unfamiliar with the achievements of the region as a whole or with parts of it outside their immediate concern. It was thought important to create a Society with which local people could identify and through which newcomers to the area could gain knowledge and familiarity with the Black Country as an entity.

Secondly, the founders believed that if the region was to have any future as a cultural influence, then it must have available publications which could be read by schools and other educational bodies and also be read by local people themselves. It was thought essential that out of print local classics should again be made available and that new publications reflecting the life of the region should be produced.

Finally, a pressing problem was the lack of representation at national level of any voice speaking for the region as a whole. To combat the fragmented state of local government in the area, it was felt that a strong organisation could speak for all the people of the region and involve itself in the general planning of the future environmental pattern of the Black Country.

In January, 1967, a few enthusiasts met at the Noah's Ark pub, Tipton, to form the Society. The response was such that energetic efforts were made to establish the organisation. In January, 1968, the first issue of *The Blackcountryman* was published and other ventures were planned in that year. Since then the Society has grown to a strength of one and a half thousand members and to be one of Britain's largest local organisations.

It is certainly the largest Society of its type in the Black Country. Its strength and its voice are devoted solely to the interests of the region and its people as interpreted by democratically elected officers and committee. With more help from all interested and concerned with the area, its work could be extended and intensified.

May we request your support?

The Blackcountryman

The Blackcountryman is the official publication of the
Black Country Society. It is supplied free of charge to all
Society members and is also on sale to members of the general
public (Price 20p). It is a fifty-six page, illustrated, quarterly
publication, with a type area of approximately 7ins. x 4¼ins.

Articles in *The Blackcountryman* cover every aspect of
life in the Black Country, past, present and future. Every issue
contains some twenty items, all *freely* contributed. Articles,
poetry, dialect ballads, short stories, anecdotes and cartoons all
have their place. New contributors are welcomed, helped, and
encouraged. Like the Society, *The Blackcountryman* has no
political, religious or racial bias.

At the present time the Society can offer all back numbers
for sale. Also an attractive, gold lettered, p.v.c. binder to hold
twelve copies of the magazine is available.